The OTHER Twelve Steps

By

Brenda Hibbs
& Jenna S. Smith

ISBN: 978-1-963179-21-7

Disclaimers

YOUTUBE: There are many YouTube videos recommended in the Resources sections of most chapters. Please note that we are not in any way affiliated with the owners of these videos, nor do we receive any remuneration from any of them.

In addition, please note that many of the YouTube videos include advertisements. We are also not affiliated with any of the purveyors of goods in these advertisements.

LEGAL CHAPTER (9): We are not legal advisors. This chapter is not intended to provide legal advice or a solution for any specific legal problems you may be facing. Rather, it's meant to offer general guidance and information about how to approach the legal system with the best attitude and strategies.

FINANCES CHAPTER (4): We are not certified public accountants (CPA) or tax professionals. The information we provide is for informational purposes only and should not be relied upon as tax or accounting advice. You should always consult a qualified CPA or tax professional for advice on your situation.

Dedication

In loving memory of Michael "Smitty" Smith, a loving Father, a vibrant rock and roll legend, and a creative soul who shared my struggle with substances and lost his battle with alcoholism way too young. Through your loss, I was inspired to fight hard and learn as much as possible where you didn't. You are a constant inspiration and ray of light in my life. Miss you and love you always. -- Jenna --

Acknowledgment

The creation of this book could not have been done without the encouragement and assistance of our friends Alex, Fred and Mister Creature and the hard work of the folks at NYT Publisher. Many thanks to all!

Introduction

Congratulations! If you have made it through rehab and have some sober time under your belt, *GREAT JOB*! Give yourself a well-deserved pat on the back. That was hard!

And it took determination and perseverance! You've demonstrated admirable willpower and taken control of your life. But beating down your addiction is just the start. What now? There's no instruction manual for picking up the broken pieces of your life and rebuilding.

You've had a powerful beginning to your journey, and it's one you can be proud of. Now, prepare yourself for the next battle: Tackling the fallout of addiction and getting your life back in order. It will take some work, but it'll be SO worth it!

You probably established a useful 'toolbox' in rehab and have learned methods for re-wiring your brain on the inside – now it's time to turn your attention outward. If you are newly out of rehab, you probably feel powerful, strong, and ready to face what's next! Good! You must maintain that strength and gather *more* tools, resources, and support. You'll need them to face the challenges life will throw at you. We hope this book will be a valuable resource to help you do that.

So, ***what*** comes next?

How do you mop up the mess created by your addiction? ***How*** do you repair burnt bridges, untangle your finances, fix your relationships, and calm the anxiety of navigating this newfound life?

What are the secret "mechanics" of transitioning into an addiction-free existence? This book is like a trail map for

your journey from rehab to real life. It's a guide to breaking old behavior patterns and building a new life based on a solid foundation of sobriety. Think of this book as an extension of your sobriety toolbox, filled with ideas and options for you to choose from.

You don't need to follow it like an instruction manual – just pick the right tools. That way, you can craft your unique road map to recovery and do one thing at a time.

The idea for this book came about when my daughter Jenna went through rehab. She came out of it buzzing with so much optimism, ready to take on the world! But we quickly realized that rehab didn't cover all the bases, and that thought was a little daunting, a bit overwhelming.

One little secret I've shared with Jenna to avoid getting overwhelmed, exhausted, or feeling like you're sinking in quicksand is to imagine an invisible tattoo across your forehead that says, "Take Care of YOU!" - a perpetual reminder that to hang on to your sobriety you'll have to get used to thinking of your own needs first, no matter what the situation, at least until your determination is stronger, you've learned to be more assertive. You have a healthy amount of self-respect!

So, when you decide, keep that invisible tattoo in mind and do what's best for YOU, even though it may initially feel quite foreign. Remember, you *deserve* to be happy! (You'll learn a lot more about this subject in Chapter 2: "Learn to Say No!")

One little nugget of wisdom from Jenna is, "Just keep trying, trying, and trying until it sticks!" It will take time and effort to rebuild your life and learn to live without the crutch of your addiction. Jenna says, "It will take as long as it takes!" If you stumble along the way, don't sweat it. Just dust yourself off and keep marching forward. And remember, small victories are still victories!

In this book, we hope you'll discover powerful ways to improve your new life. But please don't feel overwhelmed by these ideas. We suggest that you do Chapters 1 through 4 in order (they will provide a solid foundation for what comes next), but after that, just pick one that is important to you and get a start on it – then you can move on to another. One thing at a time! And as you go along, don't be afraid to ask for help – early sobriety is no place for false pride. Your family, friends, and colleagues *want* you to succeed. And health care providers have *so* many tools to add to their toolbox. Learn all you can – knowledge is power!

So, commit to putting your needs first and make self-care your new normal. Remember, change is a marathon, not a sprint, so don't expect to become an overnight superhero. Start small and take baby steps; you'll achieve your goals quickly with persistence.

If you're ready to dive headfirst into the next phase of your recovery journey, think of "The Other 12 Steps" as your dependable, friendly guide. With the same serious elbow grease, unwavering dedication, and community support that got you to this point in your addiction battle, you can hold on to your newfound sobriety and rock the happy, fulfilling life you deserve. You've got this!

Contents

Dedication ii

Acknowledgment iii

Introduction iv

CHAPTER 1 1

Nurture Your Mental Well-Being 1

CHAPTER 2 13

Learn to Say "No" Without Feeling Guilty 13

CHAPTER 3 27

Tackle That Mountain of Paperwork! 27

Whip Your Finances into Shape! 43

CHAPTER 5 61

Take Care of Your Body 61

CHAPTER 6 78

Get Your Creativity On! 78

CHAPTER 7 96

(Re)Building Positive and Strong Relationships 96

CHAPTER 8 122

It Feels Good to Look Good! 122

CHAPTER 9 135

Take Care of the Legal Stuff 135

CHAPTER 10 156

Give Back to the World 156

CHAPTER 11 176

Get An Education 176

CHAPTER 12 198

Take Care of Future You, too! 198

CHAPTER 1
Nurture Your Mental Well-Being

Addiction strips away both your physical health and your mental health. Especially in recovery, taking care of your mind is just as important as taking care of your body. Addiction may have left you with few emotional coping skills, and, being new to recovery, you may be in an emotionally vulnerable place.

The prospect of starting to take care of your mental health might feel like taking a scary leap into the unknown. You may sometimes feel lost, afraid, completely overwhelmed, or ashamed. Paying attention to your mental health can mean opening up old wounds and even being vulnerable in front of strangers.

But please be assured that these feelings are completely normal, and there are many positive steps you can take to start feeling better! Taking care of your mental health will help you cope with stress, change negative thought patterns, boost your memory and concentration, and help you get better sleep and make better decisions.

Managing stress in healthy ways will give you a feeling of accomplishment, increase your self-esteem, help you challenge those negative thoughts and replace them with more positive ones, and keep the temptation of relapse at bay, helping you stay focused on your recovery.

Here are a few ways to take care of your mental health so that you feel better overall:

Keep attending Meetings with others who are walking a similar path. There are many types of meetings to choose from.[1]

Meetings provide many benefits:

- A sense of **Fellowship** and community that can help you battle loneliness and isolation.
- **Support** from others in recovery can help you stay

[1] Check out this article from TheTemper.com: **25 Sober Communities Beyond Alcoholics Anonymous**.

on track and avoid relapse.

- **Motivation** to stay sober and continue working on your recovery. Hearing the stories of others who have successfully recovered can be quite inspiring.
- **Education** about addiction and recovery can help you understand your addiction and how to manage it.
- **Hope for the future**. Seeing others who have successfully recovered can give you hope that you can, too.
- **A chance to Contribute** and give back. You may not have thought about it, but attending meetings is not just about what you get from them. It's also about what you contribute to the group and other people's lives. Going to meetings isn't just for you; it's for the people around you, too!

> "The best way out is through."
> ***Robert Frost***

Eat a Healthy Diet

Eating nutritious foods can help improve your mood and energy levels, among many other benefits. (See Chapter 4, "Take Care of Your Body")

Spend Time in Nature

This can lighten your mood and help you see the bigger picture of your life. Incorporating time with nature into your routine can positively affect your mental health. So, make time to go for a walk, a hike on a trail, or a bike ride. Try gardening or take a chair to a nearby park and sketch. Even better, do it with a friend or two! Here are some of the many benefits of spending time in nature:

- **Reduces stress, depression, and anxiety** and can give you peace and tranquility to help calm your mind and body.
- **Improves your mood** and can provide a sense of awe and wonder that lets your positive emotions flow.
- **Increases energy levels** and can give you a sense of vitality and excitement that helps motivate and energize you.
- **Improves your sleep quality** by providing a sense of calm and relaxation that can help promote sleep.
- **Boosts creativity. Nature** can provide inspiration and new ideas that help stimulate the mind.
- **Improves focus and concentration** by giving you a sense of calm and quiet that helps block out distractions.
- **Increases lifespan:** Studies have shown that people

who spend more time in nature live longer.

Seek professional help

Especially if you are just out of rehab, it is important to seek professional help. Your addiction may have caused complete turmoil in your emotional and social life, and a therapist can help you identify and manage your symptoms and emotions and develop coping skills.

Meetings and groups are awesome, but you must find a personal counselor to help you focus your new healing power inward. Some of the hardest work is facing your deepest, darkest fears, bringing them into the light, and releasing them so you can live without that huge weight you've been carrying for so long!

Remember, too, that if you don't feel like you connect with your first counselor, try again! The right person can make a difference. Here are just a few of the things that a therapist can help you navigate:

- **Steering your way through broken relationships with family and friends -** You may think that you've burned all your bridges (and to be realistic, not all relationships will be salvageable). But you may also be surprised at how many of your family, friends, and colleagues love and respect you and have just been *waiting* for the chance to heal your relationship.

- **Learning how to relax -** Manage your thoughts and cope with difficult situations. Professionals can use techniques like Cognitive Behavioral Therapy, journaling, and positive affirmations to help you.
- **Improving your relationships -** By teaching you how to communicate better, resolve conflict, and, importantly, set boundaries.
- **Increasing your self-esteem -** By encouraging you to identify your strengths and develop a more positive outlook. Cultivating self-esteem is a journey, not a destination. It takes time and effort, but it is worth it. High self-esteem makes you feel better and more likely to achieve your goals.

Developing coping skills

To deal with difficult situations healthily, identify triggers, develop a plan to cope with them, and *be patient*. Remember, recovery is a process that takes time. There will be setbacks along the way. It is important to be patient and not give up. You are not alone! Some people care about you and want to help!

JENNA'S TAKE

"When I get negative thoughts, I consciously have to catch myself and switch gears. I think positively about myself, the future, or a situation's outcome. It took some time, but eventually, this started happening faster and without as much effort until it became a habit. And now, for my peace of mind, I carry a paraphrase of something the Dalai Lama said: "If you can't change it, why worry? If you can change it, why worry?"

Go to bed Early

As a person dealing with addiction, your sleep schedule may have been pretty chaotic. Gifting yourself the habit of consistently going to bed at a decent hour will improve your outlook and prospects. If you're not getting enough sleep, there are a few things you can do to improve your sleep habits. These include:

- **Establishing a regular sleep schedule** and sticking to it as much as possible, even on weekends.
- **Creating a relaxing bedtime routine.** This could include taking a warm bath, reading a book, or listening to calming music.
- **Make sure your bedroom is dark, quiet, and cool.** Perhaps set up your phone to play soothing nature

sounds, like ocean waves or forest sounds.

- **Avoid caffeine before bed**.
- **No devices at bedtime!** It's a good time to catch up on reading those piling-up magazines.
- **See a doctor if you have trouble sleeping**. There may be an underlying medical condition that's affecting your sleep.

Connect with others

Social support is so important for your mental health. Your addiction may have led you to feel lonely and isolated. Connecting with others will help reduce these feelings and provide community, support, motivation, and hope.

Practice mindfulness

Mindfulness is a powerful tool that can help you improve your life. There are many ways to practice mindfulness, such as meditation, focused breathing, or mindful listening. You can also find mindfulness apps and books to help you get started.

You can practice mindfulness for as little or as long as you like; the more you practice, the better you will become at it. Mindfulness is a skill that can be learned and practiced over time. Here are some tips for practicing mindfulness:

- Find a quiet place where you can relax and focus.
- Sit or lie down in a comfortable position.
- Close your eyes and take a few deep breaths.
- Pay attention to your breath as you inhale and exhale.
- Notice any thoughts or feelings, but don't judge them.
- Bring your attention back to your breath if you get distracted.
- Continue for 5-10 minutes.

Develop a hobby

We all have many talents. Develop one of yours! (See Chapter 6 – "Get Your Creativity On!) Engaging in activities that bring you joy and fulfillment will help cultivate a positive mindset.

Taking care of your mind is an invaluable investment in your overall well-being, quality of life, and your happy (maybe even joyful!) future. By prioritizing mental health, you empower yourself to navigate life's challenges with resilience, clarity, and emotional balance.

Nurturing your mind allows for self-awareness, personal growth, and the development of healthy coping mechanisms.

It enhances cognitive function, fosters meaningful relationships, and promotes productivity and accomplishment.

Remember, your mind is a powerful tool, and by giving it the care and attention it deserves, you unlock your potential for a fulfilling and purposeful existence. Embrace the journey of self-discovery, self-care, and mental well-being, and reap the benefits of a nurtured and vibrant mind!

CHAPTER 1: RESOURCES

Happify.com website: Change your brain by adopting new thought patterns and training it as if it were a muscle to overcome negative thoughts.

Headspace.com website: Hover over the "Sleep" tab at the top of their Home page, and you'll get many helpful links like HOW TO SLEEP BETTER, how to wake up easier, etc.

The Recovery Village website: This page contains a comprehensive LIST OF MENTAL HEALTH CONDITIONS. Each is linked to a very useful description page.

The American Institute of Stress website: A great LIST OF APPS for mindfulness meditation, practicing wellness, stress management, and more.

Mindfulness Exercises website: Their Free section contains a variety of AUDIO MEDITATIONS, Videos, eBooks, Quotes, and more!

National Alliance on Mental Illness website: Each section on the "YOUR JOURNEY" page has a whole list of useful information on the left-hand side.

Psychology Today website: SEARCH FOR A THERAPIST by zip code! The details given about each therapist include whether they are taking new clients, what areas they specialize in (addiction, abuse, etc.), what insurances they accept, and a general background/description.

Very Well Mind website: This page has a complete and thorough list of hotlines, same-day online therapy websites, support group resources, and more.

TED Talks website: Search for mental health, mindfulness and well-being talks.

CHAPTER 2
Learn to Say "No" Without Feeling Guilty

Brenda had trouble saying "No" for many years until she was so burnt out that she ended up in the ER with what she thought was a heart attack (thankfully, it was just a big 'ol panic attack). But she learned her lesson, started paying closer attention to her *needs,* and discovered the magic of that invisible tattoo, "Take Care of YOU!" She now easily permits herself to say "No" whenever she suspects an obligation will stress her out or drain her energy too much.

Saying "No" is like a muscle – the more you use it, the stronger it gets. Suppose you're accustomed to always saying 'yes' to everyone around you (even at the expense of your own well-being). In that case, you might feel uncomfortable or guilty saying "No" at first. But as you practice this skill, you'll realize you are *protecting your sobriety and mental health.* And that's much more important than ensuring that everyone else is happy.

Reasons why you should learn to say "No"

Because saying "Yes" to everything can:

- **Lead to over-commitment**. When you are over-committed, you are more likely to feel stressed and overwhelmed, which can lead to cravings or even relapse.
- **Make it more difficult to take care of YOU,** your primary job, this early in your recovery journey!
- **Leave you less time to care for yourself**, harming your sobriety. You might not get enough sleep, eat healthy foods, or fit in time for exercise – and you might have no time left to relax or play. You're more likely to relapse if you're tired, rundown, and frustrated.
- **Lead you into situations that are triggers** for your addiction. For example, if you are an alcoholic, saying yes to every social invitation can lead you into

situations where there will be alcohol. This can be very dangerous and make you more likely to relapse.

- **Keep you in familiar patterns** of behavior and prevent you from growing and experiencing new and exciting ways to live, love, and have fun!

If you truly want to protect your sobriety, it is *very* important to learn to say "No." Here are some tips to help you:

- **Be honest with yourself about what you want.** Before you say "Yes" to *anything*, pause and ask yourself, "Do I want to do this?" If you don't, don't be afraid to say "No."
- **Be assertive.** When you say "No," it's OK to *be clear and direct*. No need to be unkind, of course, and you don't need to make excuses or apologize. Remember, *your #1 job is taking care of YOU*, not the person asking for something or offering you something you don't want.
- **Don't be afraid to explain yourself.** If you need to explain why you are saying "No," feel free to do so. But don't feel *pressured* to justify yourself.

- **And importantly, don't be afraid to say "No" to people you care about**. Hopefully, your friends and family will be supportive enough to understand when you need to say "No" to something. It can be hard to say "No" to people we care about. Still, it is important to remember that *your sobriety is more important than their feelings*.

> *Assertiveness is the ability to express your needs and wants in a clear and direct way, without being aggressive or passive.*
>
> *(See the box in Chapter 7)*

How to establish healthy personal boundaries

Suppose you clearly define your personal boundaries, both emotional and physical, and understand what is acceptable to you and what is not. In that case, it will be easier to respectfully let people know what you are willing and unwilling to do. For example, you might say something like, "I'm happy to help out with the party, but I can't stay late," or "Thank you so much, but I've decided not to go out more than one night a week, and your invitation would be two."

- **Know what you want.** The first step to setting boundaries is to know what you want and need. What are your limits? What are your expectations? Once you know what you want, you can start communicating those things to others.
- **Be assertive.** *We're repeating this because it is such an important skill to learn.* When setting boundaries, it's very important to be assertive. This means saying "No" and standing up for yourself when your boundaries are crossed.
- **Be respectful and considerate.** When setting boundaries, respecting the other person's feelings is important. Remember that they may not be used to setting boundaries, so they may need time to adjust. A little courtesy can go a long way!
- **Be consistent.** Once you've set a boundary, it's important to be consistent. This means not letting people cross your boundaries without consequences. If you're not consistent, people will learn they can get away with crossing your boundary and be less likely to respect it.

JENNA'S TAKE

"Saying "No" without feeling guilty was hard. But the more I did it, the more I liked it! To be honest, I started before I went through rehab, with small things like saying "No" to that one extra toke of MJ. Peer pressure to be part of the 'cool kids smoke club' was huge for me. Baby steps. Over time "No, I'm good" turned into "I'm a one-hit wonder," which turned into "I'm not smoking tonight." Using the same method with alcohol was way harder and took longer, but a baby step is still a step in the right direction! It may not work for everyone, but there are many methods to try. Find one that works for you and be patient with yourself."

Some additional tips for learning to say "No":

- **Practice saying "No" in the mirror**. It may feel silly, but this can help you feel more confident when you are actually in a situation where you must say "No."
- **Create a list of reasons why you are saying "No."** Try to memorize the list; this can help you stay on track when people pressure you into saying "Yes." Brainstorm situations with a trusted friend or therapist where you might need to say "No" and determine good responses to them. Remember, declining requests or setting limits to protect your well-being is OK.

- **Find a support system.** Talk to trusted friends and family, your therapist, or your sponsor about your struggles with saying "No." They can offer you support and encouragement.

These are skills that take time and practice. **Here are some great examples of ways to be assertive and respectfully say "No":**

- "I'm sorry, but I can't attend your party tonight. I have other plans."
- "I'm not interested in going out drinking tonight. I'm trying to stay sober."
- "I'm happy to help you with your project, but I can only work on it for a little bit each day," or "I'd love to help you with that, but I'm already swamped with work."
- "I'm not comfortable lending you money. I'm trying to get my finances in order," or "I'm sorry, but I can't lend you money. I'm trying to get out of debt."
- "I'm not interested in dating right now. I'm focused on my sobriety."
- "I'm not sure if I'm comfortable with that. I'd like to think about it some more."

- "Unfortunately, my schedule/circumstances don't allow time for me to help."
- "I wish I could, but it would be too much to add to my plate."
- "I'm sorry, but I need to focus on my recovery. I'm doing very well, but I can't get sidetracked."
- "I don't want to get involved. I have enough of my drama to work on!"
- "I don't think I'm the right person for this job."
- "My mind is delicate, so I must decline."
- "There is help for you out there, but that's not me right now."
- "No, thank you. That's not my scene anymore."
- "No, thank you. I would be uncomfortable going there, but you have fun!"

Notice that in most of these instances, there are two parts: The respectful apology and the statement of what YOU want. It is important to remember that unless you're being arrested, you are not obligated to do anything you don't want to do. You have the right to say "No," you should not feel guilty about it, and you don't owe anyone an explanation for why you are saying "No."

"Half of the troubles of this life can be traced to saying "Yes" too quickly and not saying "No" soon enough."

Josh Billings

(If you struggle with saying "No," talk to your sponsor or therapist. They can help you to develop the skills you need to protect your sobriety.)

Because learning to say "NO" is an important part of recovery, let me re-emphasize: You can set boundaries and take care of YOU. If someone tries to pressure you into saying "Yes" to something you don't want to do, don't be afraid to stand up for yourself.

REMEMBER:

UNLESS YOU'RE BEING ARRESTED OR DEALING WITH THE COURT SYSTEM, YOU ARE NOT OBLIGATED TO DO ANYTHING YOU DON'T WANT TO DO!

Learn to stick up for yourself!

So, we've talked about learning to say "No" and creating healthy personal boundaries. Another important skill to learn is sticking up for yourself! You might be surprised how empowering this can be. It is vital for maintaining healthy boundaries and building self-respect. Here are some steps and strategies to help you learn to assert yourself:

- **Self-Awareness**: Start by developing self-awareness and understanding your needs, values, and boundaries. Reflect on situations where you've felt taken advantage of or disregarded, and identify areas where you want to assert yourself more effectively.
- **Confidence Building**: Build self-confidence by recognizing your strengths, accomplishments, and worth. Practice positive self-talk and affirmations to boost your self-esteem. Engage in activities that make you feel competent.
- **Effective Communication**: Learn and practice effective communication skills. Be clear, direct, and specific when expressing your thoughts, feelings, and needs. Use "I" statements to express yourself without blaming or attacking others. *(See Chapter 7)*
- **Active Listening**: Develop active listening skills to understand others' perspectives while being attentive to your needs. Practice empathy and strive for mutual understanding in conversations. *(See Chapter 7)*
- **Seek Support**: Surround yourself with supportive, understanding individuals who encourage and

validate your assertiveness. Ask your therapist or counselor to help you develop assertiveness skills and provide personalized support.

- **Role-Playing**: You can practice assertiveness in various scenarios through role-playing exercises. Enlist the help of a trusted friend, therapist, or counselor to simulate challenging situations and practice expressing your needs and boundaries.
- **Learn Conflict Resolution**: Develop skills in conflict resolution to address disagreements assertively and constructively. Focus on finding win-win solutions and maintaining respectful communication during conflicts. *(See Chapter 7)*
- **Incremental Steps**: Start by asserting yourself in less challenging situations and gradually work up to more difficult ones (practice on telemarketers!) Celebrate small victories along the way to build momentum and confidence!

Remember that, just like learning to say "No" and creating healthy boundaries, learning to stick up for yourself is a process that takes time and practice. Be patient and understand that it's normal to feel uncomfortable at first. With persistence and self-compassion, you will eventually develop the assertiveness skills needed to advocate for yourself and your well-being.

CHAPTER 2 RESOURCES

SkillsYouNeed.com article: Very comprehensive article on Assertiveness.

VeryWellMind.com website: Search for "assertiveness" or "say no" and find many useful articles.

AddictionGroup.org article: 6 Ways to Handle Triggers - This page contains information on identifying triggers and planning to handle them better.

AmericanAddictionCenters.com article: Assertiveness in Recovery – This article talks about how important assertiveness is to your recovery, including how it relates to self-esteem and the "10 Assertiveness Rights."

Westwind Recovery.com article: Setting Healthy Family Boundaries in Addiction Recovery – Includes examples of healthy boundaries and tips for setting healthy boundaries within the family.

SmallBusinessify.com article: How to Stick Up for Yourself – Sassy blog post on what it means, how to do it, and how to build confidence and courage!

HealthyPlace.com article: How to Find Courage and Confidence Without Alcohol – How to Stop Relying on Others for Confidence, Courage, and Self-esteem. Includes links to many other great articles

Put The Shovel Down video: Essential Boundaries for People in Early Recovery.

CHAPTER 3
Tackle That Mountain of Paperwork!

Yes, getting your paperwork in order might seem like a huge task. Maybe when you were in active addiction, you lost or misfiled important documents, stuffed them into random boxes, bags and even under the car seat. But clearing the clutter and getting control of your paperwork is your first step towards financial freedom! And when it's done, you will breathe such a huge sigh of relief. It'll be a real weight off your shoulders!

Just take it slow – one step at a time. Pace yourself and set aside a little time each day or each week to work on it. That way, you won't feel overwhelmed, and it will be easier to manage.

Step 1. Tools For the Task:

- **Filing Cabinet or File Boxes:** Invest in a filing cabinet or file boxes (also called 'banker's boxes') to store and organize your physical documents. Banker's boxes can be purchased at office supply stores, usually several for under $15. We live in a university town, and once a week, they open up their "Used Store," where you can purchase filing cabinets for $5.00. Look around – you may find a bargain!

- **Manila File Folders: Use** these to contain your categorized documents within the filing cabinet or file box. If you're especially nerdy about it, you can choose different colored labels to identify each category!

- **Hanging File Folders:** Also called "drop files," these are used to create Sections. For example, one *hanging folder* may be labeled "Insurance" and contain separate *manila folders* for house, car, medical, life and pet insurance. They come with plastic tabs into which you can insert a paper label. Put all the tabs right, left or center in the drawer or box.

- **File Folder Labels and/or a Label Maker:** Use labels to clearly mark your folders. A label maker is not strictly necessary but can make the process faster and more professional-looking.

- **Paper clips**, a stapler, a staple remover, pens and pencils.

- **Document Scanner:** If you prefer a digital approach, a document scanner (an actual machine or a mobile scanning app) will be needed to convert your physical documents into digital files.

- **Document Shredder:** A shredder is essential for safely disposing of documents containing sensitive information like birth dates, social security numbers or medical data. Use it to shred documents you no longer need but contain personal details. Some banks and libraries make shredders available from time to time for free.

- **Binders and binder sleeves:** Binders are useful for organizing important documents and papers you need to access frequently.
    - In one binder, you could keep *copies* of house or vehicle titles (keep the originals in a safe deposit

box at the bank), pension plan documents, social security cards (never keep yours in your wallet!), rental agreements, or legal documents like birth or death certificates, estate, adoption or divorce papers, marriage certificates, visas or passports.

  - In other binders, you could keep household papers like recipes, the kids' school papers (or even one binder for each kid), important phone numbers, babysitting instructions, coupons, gift cards, etc.

- **Filing Trays:** There is no need to do filing every day. Keep a stack of three filing trays by your computer or on your desk, labeled:
  - "To Be Filed" (try to empty it once a month)
  - "Pending" for things you are awaiting a response on.
  - "To Do" for things that need to be done soon (paying a bill, making or returning a phone call, etc.)

As each thing in "To Do" and "Pending" gets finished, they can either be discarded or put into the "To Be Filed" pile.

You can often find filing trays for cheap at second-hand stores.

An alternative to these filing trays is to keep these categories (To Be Filed, Pending and To Do) in hanging folders at the *front* of one of your filing cabinet drawers or banker's boxes.

- **Expanding File or Accordion Folder:** Use an accordion file for monthly bills. Get one with slots numbered 1 to 31 and file your bills at least 10 days before they are due, so you'll never pay them late. Each day, check the slot to see if anything is due.

That said, try to schedule automatic payments for every bill you can. It cuts down on SO much cluttery paperwork! If available, do this through your bank instead of each company separately. That way, the records of payment are all in one place.

- **Digital Storage:** You can utilize cloud storage like Google Drive, Dropbox or OneDrive to securely store digital copies of important documents. This helps create a backup and enables easy access from anywhere.
- **Calendar or Planner:** Get used to using a Calendar or Planner. A handy way to use them is to use

different colored pens for different types of appointments or for different people in the household. For instance, medical appointments could be green, while household tasks could be red, etc. Or Tom could be green, Mary could be blue, and Lisa could be red. Don't forget to schedule a time to do your filing!

These various tools are meant to assist you in organizing your paperwork effectively. You certainly don't need them all, so choose the ones that align with your preferences and needs. Adapt and customize your organizational system based on what works best for you.

JENNA'S TAKE

"To be honest, I'm still not very organized. BUT, I have spent countless hours, in small stints, going through one box or bag of papers at a time. I've thrown away a ton of old unnecessary papers, fliers, cards, news articles, magazines and letters. It started getting easier each time, and even felt good! And getting organized is a great way to let go of the past and be enthusiastic about the future. Of course, some small keepsakes to remind me of where I've been were worth holding onto. I still have more to go through, but I am reaching The End! So, my new small piles of medical, legal, auto, bills and keepsakes/memories are going to be easy to fit in any filing system I pick. It feels great! A whole new era!"

Step 2: Gather all the papers you can find and start sorting. Hey, who doesn't love a good scavenger hunt?? Look under the bed, in the closets, in the car, and anywhere you suspect might hold a cache of papers. Haul them all into a room with space to work on the floor or a large table so you can see what you have.

As you begin going through the boxes, bins and bags, first quickly separate into TWO piles: "Keep" or "Don't Keep." In the "Don't Keep" pile, put things like expired warranties, outdated statements, duplicates, any documents that are no longer relevant or required, old insurance policies, warranties for equipment you no longer have and receipts that are not for equipment, appliances, large expenses or tax deductions. You only need to keep the most current copies of bills or insurance policies; if you ever need to look back at your accounts, you can always do so online. And as you get newer ones, shred or recycle the older ones.

Put aside the "Don't Keep" pile for now (these can later be recycled or shredded), and sort the Keepers into categories such as:

- Bills (which will later go into the accordion file)
- Financial Stuff (bank statements, credit card

statements, etc.)

- Employment (pay stubs, important announcements, etc.)
- Legal (court papers)
- Utilities
- Warranties and Instructions (and the receipts that go with them)
- Vehicles
- Home/Property (rental agreement, mortgage status paperwork, property tax statements, home repair receipts, etc.)
- Coupons/Gift Cards
- Tax Documents
- Insurance papers
- School Papers (maybe a pile for each kid?)
- Medical paperwork

Take it one step at a time: Put on some music that you enjoy, and don’t try to tackle everything at once. Work on one bag or box at a time, and take a break if you're overwhelmed.

HELPFUL TIP

To avoid overwhelm, set aside a specific amount of time (say, a half hour or an hour) and try to 'schedule' your sorting a little each day. Defer the tasks you cannot complete until your next session. You may be surprised how quickly the sorting task gets done. And once you've sorted everything, you can probably maintain it in as little as 5 minutes a day!

Again, don't try to do it all at once! It could cause you way too much stress. Instead, just keep chipping away at it. Do a little each day if you can, and take breaks when you're starting to feel stressed.

Step 3: Create your filing system! Decide on a filing system that works for you. It can be a physical filing cabinet, a banker's box or a digital system using folders on your computer or in cloud storage.

- **Label your folders and file your documents:** Once you've sorted your "Keepers" and you know your categories, list them on a piece of paper. Now label all the *hanging file folder* tabs simultaneously, using the list as a reference. Use clear, descriptive labels that make it easy to locate documents when needed. Arrange the folders alphabetically, with all the tabs on the left, center or right. Now you're ready to start making individual files (*manila file folders*) to put into the hanging folders you just labeled.

For example, suppose Tom, Lisa and Mary live in your household, and they all have medical issues. You'd label a *hanging folder* "Medical." Then you'd label *manila folders* "Tom's Medical," "Lisa's Medical," and "Mary's Medical," put them all inside the Medical hanging folder, then file that hanging folder alphabetically under "M."

- **Consider digitizing:** If you prefer a digital approach, you can scan and store your documents electronically. Use a scanner or a mobile scanning app to create digital versions of your documents and save them in appropriate folders on your computer or in cloud storage.

- **Set up a maintenance routine:** After you organize everything, it would be a shame to see it slowly work its way back to chaos. So, establish a regular maintenance routine to keep it tidy. The key to maintaining an organized file system is *consistency*.

Schedule a specific time each month or week to review your To Be Filed pile (say, the last Sunday or 1st Saturday of the month, or every other Sunday, etc.). Discard what is no longer needed and file the rest in their designated folders. Make new folders as they're needed.

- **Go paperless when possible:** Consider opting for paperless statements and electronic delivery for bills and documents whenever feasible. This can help minimize future paper clutter.
- **Backup and security:** If you choose to go digital, ensure you have a backup plan to protect your files. Do regular back-ups to an external hard drive, cloud storage or both. Take precautions to secure your digital files with strong passwords and encryption.
- **Ask for help if needed:** Perhaps a friend or family member could help you organize your paperwork.

> ***HELPFUL TIP***
>
> *In order to take care of your mail without it becoming clutter, simply go through it quickly when it comes in. Recycle or discard what you can, then put the rest into your "To Do" tray for processing.*

Consider working with a professional organizer who can help you create a system for organizing your paperwork and provide support as you work through the process.

- **Which Documents You Need to Keep:** It's

important to keep certain documents for legal and financial reasons or even just a life record (like resumes or letters from loved ones). Here are some things you should keep indefinitely (or until they expire or are replaced by a newer version):

Store these in your Binder:

- Birth and death certificates
- Social security cards
- ID cards and passports
- Health Care Directives
- Green cards
- Marriage licenses
- Business licenses

Store these in your Filing System:

- Copies of vehicle titles, loan documents and repair records/receipts (until you sell the vehicle)
- Copies of house deeds and titles, mortgage documents and repair records/receipts (until you sell the house)
- Pension plan documents

- Wills, Living Wills, Trust papers and Powers of Attorney
- Letters from loved ones, newspaper clippings, mementos, etc.
- Divorce papers
- Certifications and licenses
- Court rulings
- Medical records
- Resumes
- Warranties, instructions and receipts for major items (lawn mower, blender, etc.) in case they break down and need replacement or repair.

Keep for at least a year:

- Pay stubs and bank statements
- Medical bills (keep for a year after payment in case of disputes)

Keep for at least six years after you sell:

- Home or vehicle purchase or sale documents and copies of repair or improvement documents in case of a dispute.

Keep for ten years:

- Tax records and tax receipts.

Keep the most recent version of:

- Retirement plan records (529, IRA, 401(k), etc.)
- Social Security Benefit Verification Letter Insurance Policies

If you get your records or receipts electronically or by email, print them out and put them in the file if you are using a paper filing system. If you are using electronic or cloud storage, you will need to scan in paper records.

CHAPTER 3 RESOURCES

- **Life Gets Organized video**: “How to Organize Your Filing Cabinet Files” - Quick tips to learn how to better organize your filing drawer.
- **Lea David video**: “Best Practice to Organize Your Computer Files” - How to create a streamlined and minimalist computer file management system
- **Video: “**Pendaflex Tabs to Filing Folders: How to Attach” - Quick lesson on attaching the plastic tabs to hanging file folders.
- **Terry Elisabeth video:** “DIY Hanging File Cabinet” - How to turn desk drawers into hanging file cabinets!
- **OrganiseMyHouse.com article:** “10 Simple Ways to Reduce Paper Clutter” - Simple but really effective tips and tricks to reduce paper clutter in your home once and for all.
- **Thomas Frank video:** “The Best Way to Organize Your Computer Files” - A simple process for organizing the files on your computer - and keeping them that way.
- **Nia.Nih.gov article** “Getting Your Affairs in Order Checklist: Documents to Prepare for the Future”

Alternative Filing Systems:

- **Clutterbug video:** "No Paper Piles!" - These paper organizing mistakes lead to paper clutter and paper piles. Five genius paper organizing hacks to try.
- **Cheryl Chandler video**: "Tips for Organizing a File Drawer" - Feeling overwhelmed and frustrated with household and business papers everywhere? Your clutter-free office is only one video away!
- **The Simply Organized Home video:** "How to Reduce Paper Clutter" - Ideas to sort through your paper mountains. It doesn't have to be as overwhelming and stressful as we sometimes make it out to be in our heads.
- **Thomas Frank video:** "The Best Way to Organize Your Files and Folders" - A system for organizing and digitizing your paper files.

CHAPTER 4
Whip Your Finances into Shape!

Now that your paperwork is sorted (good job!), you can start corralling your finances! You could be thinking: "Finances? That sounds so boring! And *difficult!"*

But this chapter is designed to help you, as a beginner, just take baby steps. Here, you'll find everything you need to know to start managing your money, from budgeting to saving and, eventually, investing.

But wait! "Money," you say, "what money?" Well, think about it... Now that you're not pouring copious amounts of dough into your addiction, you may suddenly find yourself in the unfamiliar position of actually *having* some money! Without learning how to manage it, though, you may find it slipping through your fingers like water through a sieve.

And before you get started, *Don't be afraid of your finances!* They're not as scary as they seem. In fact, they can be kind of fun once you get rolling. Won't it be exciting to see your credit start improving? And your debts start going down while your savings are going up?!

So relax, take a deep breath, and take one step at a time!

Part 1: Making Your Budget

A: Finish Chapter 3 (Tackle That Mountain of Paperwork)

Once you've gone through all those paper bags, shoe boxes and drawers full of papers and sorted them out, you'll be ready for Step B:

B: Take an Inventory of Your Finances.

You'll be looking for Income, Expenses and Debts. Once you have a clear picture of your financial situation, you can start paying down those debts and even saving for the future! So, let's get going – Follow these 3 steps:

Step 1: Write down all your sources of income in your notepad and add them up. You can usually find these figures by looking at your pay stubs and bank statements. Here are some typical sources of Income for the average family (just so you don't forget something):

- **Employment Income** – The primary source of Income for many households is full-time or part-time employment. This includes salaries, wages and tips earned from jobs in various industries.
- **Self-Employment Income** – Some individuals or households own businesses or work as freelancers or independent contractors. They generate income through self-employment activities such as consulting, freelance writing, graphic design or professional services.
- **Investment Income** – Some households earn Income from investments, such as stocks, bonds, mutual funds or real estate. This Income can come in the form of dividends, interest, capital gains or rental Income.
- **Retirement Income** such as pensions, annuities or Social Security.
- **Government Assistance Programs** (Like Temporary Assistance for Needy Families (TANF),

Supplemental Nutrition Assistance Program (SNAP) or housing subsidies). Yes, for your Budget, these are counted as Income.

- **Royalties:** Individuals who own intellectual property rights, such as authors, musicians or inventors, can earn Income through royalties from their work.
- **Side Jobs or Gig Economy: Many** people participate in the gig economy by taking on side jobs or temporary work, such as driving for ride-sharing services, delivering groceries, or doing freelance work through online platforms.

Step 2: Categorize your Expenses into two categories:

- **FIXED EXPENSES**: I have used Groceries, Rent, Utilities and Insurance in the example. Use as many fixed expense categories as you need.
- **VARIABLE EXPENSES:** I've used Medical, Transportation, Entertainment and Other here. You may have more variable expenses; list all you can think of.

JENNA'S TAKE

"Setting boundaries for my finances was hard. Without substances to spend my money on I found anything and everything else to spend it on instead. For me, less cash in hand was less temptation, and my money ran through my fingers like sand. But, realizing that this was a ridiculous coping method, I had to talk myself into being smarter. I tried giving myself rules like 'spend half, save half,' then 40%/60%, then 30%/70% and so on. That didn't work (go figure – I like to break rules!) For me, starting with it all in Savings makes me have to do an extra two steps before I can spend it. That's 2+ extra times I have to find a reason not to spend. So now I implement what I think of as 'Jenna's Rule of Three' that gives me 3 times to make the right decision for me; to justify my impulsiveness or not. Then I either feel good about my Buy or I feel good about my Save. Life is about choices. Give yourself as many as you can."

Step 3: Create Your Budget

A budget will help you track your money and prevent overspending. In active addiction, you may not have ever thought about how much you spent – and you may be surprised what a good feeling it is to have control of your money for a change!

To create your Budget, rough in the form below in your notebook, using whatever categories work best for you. Then do the following:

a) Write in your Total Income Amount. If you have more than one source of Income, you can list them like I did, then add them up and put the sum under Total Income.

b) Gather your debts (credit cards and loans) and list them along with their payment amounts in the Debt area.

c) List your Fixed Expenses with their monthly amounts.

d) Estimate and list your Variable Expenses. A good way to get an estimate is to look back 3 months at what those amounts have been and use averages (the total amount divided by 3) here.

e) Then add all the Debt Payments, Fixed Expenses and Variable Expenses and write that figure where it says Total Expenses (underneath Income).

f) Subtract Total Expenses from Total Income to get the Difference.

Now, divide that Difference figure however you like between your Future Expenses. Future Expenses can be anything you want to save up for. Savings are always mandatory, of course (decide what percentage or amount you would like to set aside each week or each month and put it into Savings).

BUDGET OUTLINE

INCOME		
	Social Security	1,080
	Pension	920
	Job	1,000
TOTAL MONTHLY INCOME		$3,000

EXPENSES

DEBT		FIXED		VARIABLE	
CC 6146	89	Groceries	300	Medical	50
CC 7564	148	Rent	1200	Transportation	75
Student Loan	200	Utilities	300	Entertainment	40
Personal Loan	50	Insurance	125	Other	40
Monthly Debt	487	Tot. Fixed	1,925	Total Variable	205

TOTAL MONTHLY EXPENSES $2,617

DIFFERENCE (INCOME **MINUS** EXPENSES) $383

THEN, TO SAVE FOR THE FUTURE, DIVIDE THE $383 BETWEEN:	House	Car	Vacation	Savings
	100	100	83	100

Part 2: Contact Consumer Credit Counseling

CCC agencies are nonprofit organizations that help people who are struggling with debt. We truly cannot overstate what a valuable resource these are. They can help you to get out of debt and improve your financial situation, and they offer a variety of services:

- **Budgeting assistance:** They can help you create

your Budget and stick to it. This can help you track your expenses and ensure you are not overspending.

- **Debt consolidation:** They can help you consolidate your debt into one monthly payment! This can make it *way* easier to manage your debt and save money on interest.
- **Debt settlement: They** can negotiate with creditors to lower interest rates and monthly payments. This can help you to save money on debt and get out of debt faster!
- **Credit counseling:** They can provide you with education and counseling on how to improve your credit score, which can, in turn, help you to qualify for loans and other forms of credit in the future.

Consumer Credit Counseling offices are in large and small towns all over the country. They helped Brenda immensely when she had to file for bankruptcy many years ago.

Part 3: Calculate your Net Worth.

Your Net Worth is the total value of your Assets (things you own) minus the total amount of your Debts (what you owe). To calculate your net worth, add the value of all your assets, such as your home, car, bank accounts and investments.

Then subtract the total amount of your debts, such as your mortgage, car loan, credit card debt and that loan from Uncle Tony. The Difference is your Net Worth.

IMPORTANT

Don't panic if your Net Worth is negative (you owe more than you own)! That wouldn't be surprising, as your addiction may have been adding heavily to your debt for years. The purpose of these exercises is to help you start getting a handle on it!

Now, you can start *using* these tools. The Variable Expense list will help you identify expenses that can be reduced or eliminated. The Budget will help you know how to allot your Income without overspending. And your Net Worth can help you see your progress over time as you pay down your debts.

Next, we'll look at some ways to use your new tools to begin getting your finances under control.

Part 4: Identify areas where you can cut expenses.

Now that you have a better understanding of your finances, you can start to look for ways to minimize your spending. It's a good idea now to start what is called "frugal living." This means whenever you're about to spend money, try to find either a free or an inexpensive alternative. Ask yourself questions like, “Do I really need this?” or “Is there a way I can get what I want for cheaper or free?”

When Brenda grocery shops, she still hesitates a moment before each purchase and figures out what will give her the best bargain!

Frugal Living: Some good ways to implement this new way of thinking are:

- **Cook at home more often** (Learn to shop! Learn to cook!)
- **Cancel unused subscriptions or memberships**. If you don't use them, cancel them. You might be surprised how much money you save!
- **Shop around for better deals**. Don't just accept the first price you see. Research and shop around for better deals on insurance, car repairs and other services. Need a new printer? Shop around. Need a new pair of work shoes? Shop around!
- **Use coupons and discounts.** There are many ways to get coupons and discounts. You can find them in newspapers, magazines, online, in your mailbox and on phone apps.
- **Go with Second-hand.** Almost anything you need

can be purchased second-hand. Get to know your local second-hand shops! **Buy in bulk.** If you know you'll use a lot of something, buying in bulk can save you money. However, be sure you have the space to store the items before buying them in bulk and don't buy so much that it'll go bad before you get to use it!

- **Avoid impulse purchases.** It's easy to impulse buy when you're out shopping. But before buying something, ask yourself if you really need it. Can you live without it? If you don't need it, put it back.

- **Make your own coffee and lunch.** Eating out can be expensive. If you can, make your own coffee and lunch at home. This will save you money *and* help you eat healthier.

- **Avoid debt.** Now that you know how much debt you are currently in, it is important to avoid taking on *new* debt if possible and work to pay off your current debt as quickly as possible. (See the video "Debt Snowball vs. Debt Avalanche – Which is the Best Debt Payoff Strategy?" in the Resource section at the end of this chapter.)

- **Save money.** Saving money is important for several reasons, including financial security and retirement planning. Start by setting one or more savings goals, then make a plan to reach them by setting aside either a percentage or a set amount of your monthly Income. The amount(s) you set aside each month doesn't have to be huge – even $10.00/week is a good start if that's all you can initially manage.

- **One of the best ways to save is to <u>Pay Yourself First</u>:** If it is available to you, have your paycheck directly deposited into your checking account, then set it up with your bank so that a certain amount is automatically transferred to Savings once a week, or once a month. If you automatically deposit as little as $25.00 a week into your savings account, that adds up to $1,300 in just a year!

Here are some additional tips that may be helpful:

- **Be patient.** It takes time, determination and self-discipline to get control of your finances and to save money. Don't be discouraged if you don't see results immediately. Just keep working at it, and you will eventually reach your goals.

- **Don't give up.** There may be times when you want to. But it is important to remember *why* you are trying to get control of your finances in the first place. Keep your goals in mind; don't give up!

- **Review your finances regularly,** once a month or once a quarter, to make sure they are on track. This will help you identify any problems early on and adjust as needed.

- **Celebrate your successes!** As you reach your financial goals, say, paying off a credit card, take some time to celebrate your success to help you stay motivated and on track.

Getting control of your finances can be a challenge, but it is definitely possible and really worth the effort. By following these tips, you can regain control of your financial life and build a brighter future!

As you get better control of your finances, you will be able to take some additional steps to improve your credit:

- **Pay your bills on time.** This is the most important thing you can do to improve your credit score.

- **Keep your credit utilization low.** Credit utilization is the amount of credit you use compared to the amount of available credit. Aim to keep your credit utilization below 30%.

- **Create a credit history.** If you don't have any credit history, you can start by getting a secured credit card. This type of credit card requires you to make a deposit, which will be your credit limit. Once you have it, use it responsibly. Try to pay off the balance every month.

- **Get a copy of your credit report.** You can get a free copy of your credit report from each of the three major credit bureaus once per year. Review your credit report for any errors and dispute them if you find any. You can dispute errors online, by mail or by phone.

Here are some additional tips that may help you improve your credit:

- **Sign up for credit monitoring.** Credit monitoring services can alert you to any changes to your credit report, such as new accounts or late payments. This can help you to catch any problems early on and take action to correct them. Brenda is a huge fan of Credit Karma, but many other monitoring services are available.

- **Use a credit builder loan.** This is a tool that helps people with bad credit improve their credit scores. It works simply: you borrow a small amount of money (which is kept in a 'locked' savings account) and make monthly payments to pay it back. The lender then reports your on-time payments to the credit bureaus, which can help improve your credit history. You get the loan amount back, plus interest, minus any fees at the end of the payoff period.

- **Get a co-signer.** If your credit history is less than stellar, you may need to get a co-signer on a loan or credit card. A cosigner is someone who agrees to assume responsibility for the debt if you default on the loan or credit card. Even if you have poor credit, having a co-signer may help you get approved for a loan or credit card. Remember, this is a big ask of your co-signer since their credit will be impacted if you default. Improving your credit score will take time and dedication, but if you follow these suggestions, you can boost your score and increase your chances of being approved for loans and other forms of credit. Just remember to be patient and persistent, and your credit score will rise!

CHAPTER 4 RESOURCES

Learning to Budget:

- **BetheBudget.com** - 7 Easy Budgeting Tips for Beginners
- **NerdWallet.com** - Budgeting 101: How to Budget Money
- **FrugalFanatic.com** - Budgeting for Beginners: A Practical Guide to Get Started

Improving your Credit:

- **ConsumerCredit.com** – Consumer Credit Counseling is a service offered by non-profit agencies to help consumers take back control of their finances. Credit counselors are certified financial professionals with expertise in helping consumers understand their financial situation, how they got there, and the options for improving their financial lives.

- **CreditKarma.com** – Free access to your daily credit score and listings of available credit cards, including secured cards.
- **NerdWallet.com – How to improve your credit Fast!**

Frugal Living:

- **WiseBread.com** - "Stretch that dollar in style without sacrificing your favorite luxuries." Frugal experts show you how to live large on a small budget.
- **ThePennyHoarder.com** – Article: "This Couple Saves 70% of Their Incomes — Here's Exactly How They Do It"
- **Youtube.com** – Listed results for "frugal living in sobriety"

Handling Finances in Recovery:

- **TheTemper.com** – Two articles: "Overcoming Debt" and "How to Save (or Spend) All That Money You're Not Using to Buy Booze."
- **MoneyGeek.com** - "Financial Guide for Those Recovering from an Addiction"
- **CreditCards.com** – "How to rebuild your finances after rehab"
- **AmericanAddictionCenters.org** – Article: "Guide to Personal Finance in Recovery" (Quote: "Starting small still means starting *somewhere*.")

Saving Money:

- **AARP.org** - 99 Great Ways to Save
- **RamsaySolutions.com** - "How to Save Money: 23 Simple Tips"
- **NerdWallet.com** - How to Save Money Now (Before You Really Need It)
- **Huffpost.com** - 27 Awesome Ways to Trick Yourself into Saving Money

CHAPTER 5
Take Care of Your Body

Taking care of your body is an important part of addiction recovery. Your body has been through a lot, and giving it the time and attention it needs to heal is important. There are many things you can do to achieve wellness in recovery. Here are just a few:

Part 1: Eat a healthy diet

This is essential for overall health and well-being. When you're in recovery, it's important to make sure you're getting enough fruits, vegetables and whole grains. You should also limit processed foods, sugary drinks and unhealthy fats.

- **Make gradual changes**. Don't try to change your entire diet overnight. Start by making small changes, such as adding more fruits and vegetables to your meals or cutting back on processed foods.

- **Read food labels**. When you're shopping for food, take the time to read food labels. This will help you make informed choices about what to buy.
- **Cook more meals at home**. When you cook at home, you have more control over the ingredients that go into your food; this makes it easier to eat healthily. And cooking is fun!
- **Plan your meals ahead of time**. Knowing what you will eat makes you less likely to reach for unhealthy snacks or meals.
- **Find healthy recipes that you like**. There are many healthy recipes available online and in cookbooks. Find some recipes you enjoy and make them part of your diet.
- **Don't be afraid to ask for help**. If you're struggling to make healthy changes, don't be afraid to ask for help from a registered dietitian or other healthcare professional.

Part 2: Get regular exercise

Exercise is another important part of addiction recovery. It helps to improve your physical and mental health. Don't go overboard at first, though. Thirty minutes of moderate-intensity exercise most days of the week is a great goal to aim for.

- **Find an activity you enjoy**. There are many different types of exercise, so it's important to find one you enjoy. You're less likely to stick with your workout if you don't enjoy it. Try first taking a 15- or 30-minute walk or bike ride. Who knows, you might get to know your neighbors!
- **Start slowly**. If you're not used to exercising, start slowly. Gradually increase the intensity and duration of your workouts. If you're going for a walk, don't be embarrassed to stop and rest when needed. Or if you're riding a bike, don't be embarrassed to walk the bike part of the time.
- **Make exercise a part of your routine**. Schedule time for exercise in your day just like any other important appointment. And as your sleep routine straightens out, you may have some time in the morning or evening that you didn't have before.
- **Find a workout buddy**. Working out with a friend can help you stay motivated and accountable. Perhaps someone you've become acquainted with at Meetings has similar goals, schedule and personality.

JENNA'S TAKE

"In early sobriety I replaced substance abuse with food abuse, so naturally I gained weight. I also recoiled from almost all of my usual activities, physical and social. So, when I determined to stop abusing food, I started with a healthy diet in mind. I also started going to the doctor regularly. They helped me find out what vitamins my body was lacking so that I could give my metabolism a boost with the right vitamins and minerals, and eat food that would help instead of hinder.

After a year or more of steady physical care and attention I am glad to say that I've dropped some of the weight and am steadily gaining energy. I'm the healthiest I have been in a long time. Now I can switch focus to a good workout routine to gain back flexibility and muscle. I'm also dipping back into socializing and counseling to hopefully continue to rediscover myself. One thing at a time will eventually come together to make a whole me! Patience is such an important tool for success."

- **Set realistic goals.** Don't try to do too much too soon. Start with small goals, such as walking for 15 to 30 minutes three times a week, and gradually increase your activity level.

- **Don't give up.** It takes time to build the habit of exercise. Don't get discouraged if you miss a workout or two. Just get back on track and keep going.

Part 3: Get enough sleep

Getting enough sleep is a vital part of addiction recovery, too. Sleep is essential for your body to heal and repair itself. Getting at least 7-8 hours of sleep each night is important to give your body the time and attention it needs to heal.

- **Stick to a regular sleep schedule.** Go to bed and wake up at the same time each day, even on weekends. This will help to regulate your body's natural sleep-wake cycle.
- **Create a relaxing bedtime routine.** This could include taking a warm bath, reading a book, or listening to calming music. Avoid watching TV or using electronic devices in the hour before bed, as the blue light emitted from these devices can interfere with sleep.
- **Make sure your bedroom is dark, quiet and cool.** Darkness helps to promote melatonin production, a hormone that regulates sleep. Noise and light can disrupt sleep, so make sure your bedroom is as dark and quiet as possible. A cool temperature is also ideal for sleep.
- **Avoid caffeine before bed.** Caffeine is a stimulant that can make it difficult to fall asleep. It does this by blocking the effects of adenosine, a

neurotransmitter that makes you feel sleepy. Caffeine can also stay in your system for several hours, so even if you have it in the afternoon, it can still make it difficult to fall asleep at night.

- **Get regular exercise.** Exercise can help to improve sleep quality. However, avoid exercising too close to bedtime, as this can make it difficult to fall asleep.
- **See a doctor.** If you struggle to get enough sleep, talk to your doctor. There may be an underlying medical condition that is interfering with your sleep.

Part 4: Manage your stress

We all, of course, have stress, which can be a major trigger for relapse. It's very important to find healthy ways to manage stress in addiction recovery. Here are some ways to keep stress to a minimum:

- **Talk to someone you trust.** Talking about your feelings can help you to process them and feel less stressed. Talk to a trustworthy friend, family member, therapist, or anyone else you feel comfortable talking to.
- **Exercising regularly, eating a healthy diet and getting enough sleep** can help you manage stress, as can staying hydrated and taking breaks when needed.

These ways of taking care of yourself will help you to feel better and be better able to cope with stress.

- **Practice relaxation techniques.** Many relaxation techniques can help reduce stress, such as meditation and deep breathing. Find a technique that works for you and practice it regularly.
- **Set small goals.** Don't do too much too soon. Set small goals, such as eating one healthy meal a day or going for a short walk once a day.
- **Be patient.** It takes time to heal from addiction. Don't get discouraged if you don't see results immediately. Just keep taking care of yourself, and eventually, you will see improvement.

Part 5: Go see some doctors!

When you were in active addiction, getting the healthcare you needed may have been a struggle. Some things that may have made it difficult for you to get good healthcare in the past are:

- **Transportation:** If you do not have a car or access to public transportation, getting to appointments can be difficult. If this is the case for you, contact your health insurance company. Many health insurance companies and local governments offer transportation assistance programs to help people get to their medical appointments. If you are over 55, see if any transportation services are available through your local senior center.

- **Cost:** Medical appointments can be expensive, and if you don't have insurance, you may not be able to afford them. (See the section on Finding Health Insurance below.)
- **Time:** Medical appointments can take a lot of time, and if you are working or taking care of other responsibilities, you may find it difficult to find the time to go. Try to plan ahead. Schedule your appointments as far in advance as possible so that you can work them into your schedule.
- **Motivation:** You may not have had the motivation to go to appointments. Some ways to muster up motivation are to plan, set a goal, or tell someone you trust. Remember why you are in recovery; don't be afraid to ask for help. And when it's done, reward yourself!
- **Shame:** Maybe you felt ashamed of your addiction, so you didn't want to go to appointments because you feared being judged. You can combat this feeling by challenging negative thoughts, focusing on your

progress, seeking support and practicing self-compassion.

There are many important reasons for you to get the medical support you need to help you stick with your recovery:

- Addiction may have harmed your physical health. People addicted to drugs and alcohol are more likely to experience health problems like liver disease, heart disease and cancer. Getting regular healthcare can help you identify and treat health problems early on.
- It can also have a negative impact on your mental health. Folks who struggle with addiction are also more likely to experience mental health problems such as depression, anxiety and post-traumatic stress disorder (PTSD). Getting the mental health care you need can help identify and treat these problems, improving your overall well-being and making staying in recovery easier.
- To prevent relapse: Relapse, of course, is *the* big challenge in addiction recovery. Regular healthcare can help you identify and address risk factors for relapse, such as stress, boredom and social isolation, which, in turn, can help you develop coping mechanisms for dealing with these challenges and

reducing the risk of relapse.

- Addiction can also lead to social problems. People who are actively using drugs and alcohol are more likely to lose their jobs, their homes and their relationships. Regular healthcare can help you address these social problems and improve your quality of life.

- Addiction is a chronic disease, but it is possible to recover. Recovery is a lifelong process that requires ongoing effort and support. Regular healthcare can help you stay on track and maintain your sobriety.

Some types of medical care you might consider are:

A Primary Care physician

A PCP is a doctor who provides general medical care. They are most people's first point of contact when sick or injured. PCPs can:

- Diagnose and treat various medical conditions, including common illnesses, injuries and chronic diseases.

- Provide preventive care, such as vaccinations and screenings.

- Order and interpret tests

- Prescribe medications
- Provide counseling and education
- Make referrals to specialists
- Coordinate with other providers

A Dentist

Dentists provide a variety of services, including:

- Preventative care
- Diagnosis and treatment
- Restorative and cosmetic dentistry
- Oral surgery and rehabilitation
- Education and counseling as it pertains to dental hygiene.

An eye doctor (Ophthalmologist)

The services ophthalmologists provide help patients maintain good eye health and prevent eye problems. By providing comprehensive care, ophthalmologists provide services like:

- Eye exams to assess vision and detect any eye problems.
- Prescribing glasses and contact lenses to correct

vision problems.

- Treating eye diseases such as cataracts, glaucoma and macular degeneration.
- Performing surgery: They perform a variety of eye surgeries, including cataract surgery, glaucoma surgery and corneal transplants.
- Providing education and counseling to patients about eye health and how to prevent eye problems.

Finding Health Insurance

This can be a challenge, and not just for those in recovery! Here are some tips on how to go about it:

- Check with your employer. Many employers offer health insurance to their employees. If you are employed, check with your employer to see if they offer health insurance.
- Look into government programs. There are a number of government programs that can help people in recovery get health insurance. These programs include Medicaid, Medicare and the Children's Health Insurance Program (CHIP). Another good place to check is the County health department.
- Shop for health insurance on your own. Websites like

HealthPlans.com and HealthCare.gov let you shop for health insurance independently. These websites can help you compare plans and find one that fits your needs.

- Talk to a health insurance agent. A health insurance agent can help you find a plan that fits your needs. They can also help you understand the different plans and how they work, assist you in signing up and let you know when or how to re-up.

It is important to note that not all health insurance plans cover addiction treatment. If you are in recovery and looking for health insurance, check the plan to see if it's covered.

Here are some additional tips for finding health insurance in recovery:

- Be honest with your insurance company about your history of addiction. This will help them to determine which plan is right for you.
- Ask about discounts. Many health insurance companies offer discounts to people in recovery. Ask about any discounts that they offer.
- Consider a high-deductible plan. High-deductible plans can be a good option for people in recovery.

These plans have lower monthly premiums, but they have higher deductibles. If you are healthy and do not expect to need a lot of medical care, a high-deductible plan may be a good option.

- Look for a plan with a good network of providers so that you will be able to see the doctors and other healthcare providers that you need.

Although finding health insurance in recovery can be challenging, it is important to remember that you are not alone. Many resources are available to help you find a plan that fits your needs. Just be persistent!

Taking care of your body is super important in addiction recovery because it can help you to feel better physically and mentally. When you are taking care of your body, you are giving yourself the best chance of staying sober!

CHAPTER 5 RESOURCES

Eat a Healthy Diet:

- **Mountainside Treatment Center video:** Nutritionist's Guide to Addiction Recovery and Nutrition – Two minutes unbelievably packed with info!
- **Dr. K. J. Foster's video:** Nutrition in Early Recovery - Elements that will help you to successfully stay clean and sober, prevent relapse, and help you to develop more POWER in your recovery.
- **American Addiction Centers article:** Diet and Nutrition in Recovery – Covers diet-related symptoms of substance abuse.

Get Regular Exercise

- **Hazelden Betty Ford Foundation video:** Fitness in Sobriety and Recovery from Addiction
- **The Phoenix is a sober, active community website.** Since 2006, they've been helping people rise above the ashes of addiction through physical fitness.
- **Tree House Recovery -** Why Fitness is Essential to

Lasting Addiction Recovery. When your body and mind are strong, life is limitless!

Getting Enough Sleep

- **American Addiction Centers -** Sleep and Addiction Recovery: Benefits and Tips for Better Sleep
- **VeryWellMind.com -** How to Ease Withdrawal Insomnia During Recovery
- **Purple.com -** How Addiction and Substance Abuse Affect Sleep

Manage Your Stress

- **DrugRehab.com** – Stress and Addiction
- **RecoveryBayCenter.com -** 10 Stress Management Techniques for Addiction Recovery – Learn healthy ways to combat stress.
- **SoundRecoveryCenters.com -** 20 Ways to Relax: Addiction Treatment Relaxation Techniques

Go See Some Doctors!

- **RehabAfterWork.com -** Why You Need to Talk to Your Doctor About Your Addiction
- **HarrisHouseSTL.org -** Why Dental Health Matters in Addiction Recovery

- **ReviewOfOptometry.com** – How Drug Abuse Affects the Eye

CHAPTER 6
Get Your Creativity On!

For several years now, Brenda has been meeting every Thursday afternoon with 3 or 4 friends to sketch or paint. In the winter, they do "art on Zoom," and when the weather is nice, they choose a local park and take their chairs and supplies to sit around in the shade, visiting and painting. It's really lovely – a snippet of time spent NOT rushing around taking care of life's toils.

She could still connect with her friends through this little ritual, even when fighting cancer and pain. It provided a bit of refreshment from her circumstances and a nice morale boost!

In your battle to hang on to your sobriety, you may not have considered trying to fold some creativity into your life. Try it! Maybe there's something you've always wanted to try or something that you used to do that got left by the wayside of addiction. Pick it up again! Think about what you loved to do as a child. What were some of your favorite activities? Cooking? Painting? Gardening? Woodworking? Music? Once you start, you might be surprised how quickly those old passions can be reignited!

When Brenda first started painting with her friends, she didn't really know what she wanted to do. She'd had a bad experience in the past using oil paints but knew she was smart and creative, so she decided to give it another try. It went WAY better than she thought it would! So much so that, after about 6 months of doing little oil paintings (with some so-so results, but some that she loved!), she decided to take up watercolors instead to keep expanding her skill set, which went well, too. Then she remembered that she loved doing pen and ink work when she was younger. So now, when she meets for "art in the park," she does almost exclusively pen and ink work. We tell this little story to illustrate what the creative process can be like if you just give it a chance!

So, what is creativity? It's the ability to come up with new and original ideas. And for people in recovery, it can be a valuable tool. Why? Because it can help you explore your thoughts and process your experiences in healthy ways. Whether through art, writing, music, or movement, creativity offers a means of self-expression that can be deeply healing. Creativity can also help you to connect with others in recovery and find new perspectives on your life, and it can help you:

- **Express yourself: Creativity** can be a powerful way to express emotions that are difficult to put into words. This can be especially helpful for people who have been suppressing their emotions for a long time.

- **Cope with difficult emotions:** Creativity can be a healthy way to cope with emotions such as anger, sadness and anxiety. It can help you to process your emotions safely and constructively.

- **Find new ways of living:** Creativity can help you find new passions and hobbies that can bring joy and fulfillment to your life and help you build a new, meaningful life outside of addiction.

JENNA'S TAKE

"Being a creative type, I have done SO many things in my life to express my creativity, which slowly shut down the deeper into addiction and depression I allowed myself to sink. Once I reached an ultimate bottom, it was really hard to get excited about anything!!!

So, I ended up saying to myself, "What makes me feel good? What makes me happy every time I do it? What never feels like a chore? What is my joy? My happy place? For me, the answer was gardening. A quiet place to meditate or play and sing my favorite tunes while dancing and getting the earth between my fingers and toes. It felt so satisfying/gratifying to see things grow and be able to share with friends and family. I still have high hopes for a comeback of other creative outlets and hobbies I used to enjoy. But my Happy Place, gardening, will always bring me personal peace and satisfaction."

- **Build self-esteem: When** you create something, you are essentially saying, "I *am* capable of doing this," which can help you to feel good about yourself and your abilities and boost your self-esteem.
- **Connect with others:** When you share your creative work, you open yourself to feedback and connection. This can help you to build relationships and feel supported.

- **Improve mental and physical health: Creativity** has been shown to improve mental and physical health by reducing stress, anxiety and depression. It can also improve sleep, boost the immune system and even reduce pain!

Because you are in addiction recovery, we strongly encourage you to explore your creative side. We all have many talents, even though you may think otherwise – find and develop one of yours! There are SO many ways to be creative; find something that feels good to you. Creativity can be *such* a powerful tool for healing and recovery!

Remember, each person's recovery journey is unique. If you are interested in joining a creative therapy group, finding one that aligns with your specific needs and preferences may take time. Persistence and reaching out to multiple sources will increase your chances of finding a suitable art therapy group for your recovery journey.

Here are some examples of types of creative therapy groups you may find interesting:

ART THERAPY can help people process traumatic experiences, cope with stress and develop coping skills.

Try some of these ways to connect with an art therapy group:

- **Reach out to treatment centers** and ask if they offer or can recommend art therapy groups for individuals in recovery.
- **Search online directories** specifically focused on art therapy and support groups. For instance, the American Art Therapy Association has search features that allow you to find art therapy groups in your area.
- **Contact local art organizations**, art schools, or community centers that offer art programs.
- **Attend support group meetings.** While these groups may not be specifically focused on art therapy, you can connect with individuals who might be aware of local resources or art-based recovery programs.
- **Consult with your therapist or counselor.** Discuss your interest in art therapy and ask if they can recommend any groups or professionals in this area.
- **Explore online platforms and forums** dedicated to art therapy in recovery. They can provide support, resources or even virtual art therapy experiences. Engaging with these communities can connect you with like-minded individuals and potentially lead to

discovering local art therapy groups.

MUSIC THERAPY is a therapeutic approach that utilizes the power of music to assist individuals in expressing themselves and navigating their emotions. It can be helpful for people in addiction recovery for the same reason art therapy is beneficial.

How can you find a music therapy group? In many of the same ways listed above to find an art therapy group, you can:

- **Reach out to local music organizations**, music schools or community centers that offer music programs to ask if they know of any music therapy groups
- **Consider participating in virtual music therapy sessions.** These can provide a safe and supportive space to explore the power of music for healing and recovery. (And check out the Resources at the end of this chapter!)

WRITING as a creative expression can be highly beneficial for individuals in addiction recovery in several ways:

- **Self-Reflection and Insight:** Writing provides a medium for self-reflection, allowing individuals to explore their thoughts, feelings and experiences related to addiction and recovery. Through writing, you can gain a deeper understanding of yourself and your triggers, patterns and motivations. It can help uncover underlying emotions and provide insights into the recovery journey.

- **Emotional Release and Processing**: Writing offers a safe space to express and release your emotions. It allows you to channel your feelings, frustrations and challenges onto the page, providing a sense of catharsis. By putting words to your experiences, you can gain a sense of relief, release emotional burdens and work through difficult emotions associated with addiction and recovery.
- **Storytelling and Narrative Transformation**: Writing can enable you to shape your own narratives. By telling your stories through written words, you can reframe your experiences, reclaim your identity and rewrite your personal narratives in a more empowering and positive light. The process of writing your story can help you feel more in control of your life, hopeful about the future and proud of your accomplishments.
- **Increased Self-Awareness and Insight**: You can develop a heightened sense of self-awareness through regular writing. By documenting your

thoughts and experiences, you can track your progress and identify patterns, triggers and potential relapse warning signs. This awareness can help you make more informed choices and develop effective coping strategies to maintain your sobriety.

- **Accountability and Goal Setting**: Writing can serve as a tool for setting goals and holding yourself accountable in recovery. By writing aspirations, intentions and action plans, you can solidify your commitment to recovery and track your progress, providing a sense of structure, focus and motivation in achieving your goals.
- **Connection and Support**: Sharing written work in support groups or therapy sessions can foster a sense of connection and support among individuals in recovery. It allows for the exchange of experiences, insights and encouragement. Additionally, reading the works of others who have gone through similar experiences can provide inspiration, validation and a sense of community.

Writing can take various forms in addiction recovery, such as journaling, creative writing, poetry or personal essays. Regardless of the form, writing can be a powerful and therapeutic tool for self-discovery, emotional expression and personal growth throughout your recovery journey.

DANCE in addiction recovery can take various forms, such as structured dance classes, ballroom dance, tango, expressive movement therapy or informal freestyle dancing. The specific benefits will vary for each individual, but dance as a creative expression can contribute positively to your recovery by promoting self-expression, emotional well-being, physical health and social connection. Our local university has periodic dance events open to the public, sometimes with a lesson before the event starts. If you live in a college town, check it out!

OTHER CREATIVE ACTIVITIES

Many other creative activities can be helpful for people in addiction recovery. Some examples include:

- **Photography** – Photography can be a way to express your emotions, thoughts and experiences nonverbally. This can be especially helpful if you struggle to understand your feelings.
- **Cooking** – Cooking can be a great way to connect with other people who share a common interest. Joining a cooking class or group can be a great way to meet new people and make friends.

- **Gardening** – When people see their plants growing and thriving, it can boost their self-confidence and make them feel good about themselves. This can be especially helpful for people who have struggled with low self-esteem.
- **Quilting** – Quilting is a complex process that requires various skills, such as sewing, cutting and piecing. Learning these skills can help you to feel more confident and capable.
- **Games** – Games can teach you various skills, such as problem-solving, critical thinking and teamwork. These skills can be helpful in all areas of life, including recovery. Think playing cards, bowling, basketball… indoor games or outdoor games!
- **Needlework** – Needlework can be a great way to relax and de-stress. The repetitive movements and the focus on detail can help you to clear your mind and focus on the present moment.
- **Woodworking or pottery throwing** – These often require patience and perseverance. They teach individuals the value of persistence and the rewards of delayed gratification.
- **Knitting or Crocheting** – Engaging in knitting or crocheting requires concentration and focus on the

present moment. The craft's rhythmic nature can be a healthy distraction from intrusive thoughts or urges.

- **Sewing** – Acquiring sewing skills not only promotes self-sufficiency but also increases self-confidence and a sense of competence.
- **Flower arranging** – By engaging in flower arranging, you can immerse yourself in a creative, therapeutic and nature-inspired activity that promotes mindfulness, emotional healing, self-expression and a sense of accomplishment.

Finding a balance between challenge and comfort is important when starting a new creative endeavor. Don't feel like you must jump in with the most complex projects; start small and allow yourself to grow into your creative passion. Any artistic expression, no matter how simple, can bring joy and fulfillment into your life, help you explore your emotions, and heal from addiction. So, take your time, have fun, and enjoy the journey of self-discovery that comes with creative expression!

CHAPTER 6 RESOURCES

GETTING ALL CREATIVE IN RECOVERY:

- **Avalon Recovery Society** – The Power of Creativity in Sobriety
- **Granite Recovery Centers** - The Role of Creativity in the Recovery Process
- **HerrenWellness.com** - The Healing Power of Creativity in Recovery
- **TheTemper.com** - 5 Ways to Tap into Creativity in Sobriety
- **Tree House Recovery** - Reconnecting with Creativity in Sobriety

ART THERAPY:

- **American Art Therapy Association** – How to Find an Art Therapist
- **AvalonMalibu.com** - 5 Amazing Art Projects to Jump-Start Your Recovery
- **Dr Second Chance video** - Art Therapy for Addiction Recovery

MUSIC THERAPY:

- **Recovery Unplugged** - The first and only addiction treatment organization to fully utilize music in rehab.

Check out their video playlist of "Life in Recovery" and "Life After Treatment."

- **American Music Therapy Association** – Hiring a Music Therapist: What, Who, Where, How and Why.
- **TheRecoveryVillage.com** - 5 Reasons Why Sobriety and Music Connect Well

WRITING:

- **FhereHab.com** – 20 Journaling Prompts that Support Recovery
- **WritersForRecovery.org** - Discover the power of the written word to process trauma, build self-esteem, and promote a healthy image of people in recovery.
- **PsychologyToday.com** - Writing for Addiction Recovery: How Journaling Exercises Increases Sobriety

DANCE:

- **Recovery.org** – The Healing Power of Dance Movement Therapy
- **BanyanTreatmentCenter.com -** With dancing, you can put into motion the thoughts and feelings that you don't know quite how to say.
- **Rehabs.com** - Your Ultimate Guide to Daybreaker Sober Dance Parties

- **MeetUp.com** – Use the search function at the top left of the page to find sober dance opportunities near you!

PHOTOGRAPHY:

- **DesignSwan.com** – How Using Photography Can Help in Addiction Recovery
- **HyperAllergic.com** – An Artist's Opiate Addiction Recovery Through Photography
- **Chestnut.org** - Mindful Photography and Addiction Recovery

COOKING:

- **ThePhoenixRC.com** – Addiction Recovery Cookbook
- **Food-Management.com** - Cooking for Recovery After Addiction
- **Facebook.com – Sober Chefs**: This group was created for people in recovery from addiction who have discovered and come to appreciate their love for good food and cooking.

GARDENING:

- **CanyonVista.com** - Ideas for a variety of types of gardens

- **ChoiceHouseColorado.com** - Community gardening manages to accomplish both the social and sober needs of what can otherwise be an isolating time.
- **BelaireRecovery.com** - Get Things Growing: How Gardening Supports Your Sobriety

QUILTING:

- **QuiltingBoard.com** – Twenty pages of quilting tutorials, plus message boards and Forums.
- **YouTube.com** – Search results for "quilting tutorials for beginners"
- **QuiltingHub.com** – One-stop shop for quilting blogs all over the world!

GAMES:

- **12KeysRehab.com** – This article, "Fun Sober Activities," is chock full of ideas for activities, including games.
- **FunPartyPop.com** – Positive Printable Recovery Games and Activities
- **JoinMonument.com** - 25 Sober Activities That Are Fun & Fulfilling

NEEDLEWORK:

- **Herrschners.com** – A variety of needlework kits, including counted cross stitch, embroidery, punch needle and needlepoint.
- **Etsy.com** – Results of a search for "beginner needlework." Pages contain kits and PDFs for cross stitch, needlepoint, etc.
- **Needlepointers.com** - 600+ Free Needlework Patterns and Projects. MANY types of needlework to explore!

WOODWORKING:

- **SperoRecovery.org** - 5 Psychological and Social Benefits of Woodworking
- **AddictionRecoveryeBulletin.org** – Article "Artist Uses Woodworking to Overcome Addiction."
- **eZineArticles.com** – Article: "I Believe in You: A Woodworker's Approach to Sobriety"

KNITTING AND CROCHETING:

- **TheTemper.com** – Article: "Finding Joy in Sobriety Through Knitting; All of the benefits of knitting as a form of mindful meditation"
- **YouTube.com video** - "Crochet VS Knitting - Which Is Best for Absolute Beginners?

- **Blog.LionBrand.com** - 10 Most Important Health Benefits of Yarn crafting

SEWING:

- **SewDaily.com** – Article: "Sewing for Mental Health — How Sewing Can Improve Your Mood"
- **MindFood.com** – Article: "5 Health Benefits of Sewing"
- **TheGuardian.com** – Article: "The calming effects of sewing can help people express and heal themselves. How absorbing your concentration in needlework relieves inner turmoil."

FLOWER ARRANGING:

- **DallasNews.com** – Article: "'It's almost like a drug': How flower arranging is helping people relieve stress. Flowering arranging offers moments of stillness and mindfulness.
- **SageLife.com** – Article: "The Benefits of Flower Arranging"
- **Gardenista.com** – Article: "Flower Arrangements 101: A Crash Course for Easy and Elegant Florals"

CHAPTER 7
(Re)Building Positive and Strong Relationships

The task of fixing broken relationships may seem daunting (and it is, indeed, complex), but the effort and courage required to embark on this journey will be incredibly rewarding. It's natural to experience emotions like shame or stigma while navigating this part of your recovery process, and trust issues may arise both for you and the other people in your life. Feelings of betrayal may linger, making it challenging to rebuild trust (and to be realistic, it may be that not all your relationships will be repairable). However, with determination and open communication, the process of mending relationships can lead to healing, renewed connections and even new ones!

When you are newly out of rehab, the thought of straightening out relationships can be as intimidating as climbing Mount Everest in stilettos. But you have to start somewhere, and we're hoping this chapter, with its focus on mending burnt bridges, will give you the start, tools and encouragement you need.

The method of mending relationships outlined in this chapter will consist of three sections:

1. Self-Forgiveness;

2. Identifying the people you want to reconnect with, as well as the issues to be addressed with each one, and

3. Tips and Tools for effective communication. (Consider using "The Other Twelve Steps Workbook" to help you.)

MOVE ON WITH SELF-FORGIVENESS

Why self-forgiveness first? Because it is one of the most foundational aspects of recovery. When you're able to forgive yourself for your past mistakes, you can begin to move forward with your life and be more comfortable in your own shoes, so to speak. Self-forgiveness does not mean forgetting what happened or condoning the behavior. It simply means letting go of the anger, guilt and shame that can hold you back. Here are some ways to help you get used to forgiving yourself:

- **Acknowledge your mistakes -** This is the first step to self-forgiveness. It doesn't mean that you have to beat yourself up, but it does mean honestly taking responsibility for your actions. Here are some things you can try to get that self-forgiveness ship sailing:
- **Identify the mistakes** – The first step to acknowledging a mistake is to identify what you did wrong. This can be difficult, especially if you are feeling defensive or embarrassed. However, it is important to be honest with yourself about what happened. You might be surprised what a relief it can be just writing them down and getting them out of your brain.
- **Take responsibility** – Once you have identified a mistake, it is important to take responsibility for your actions. This does not mean that you must be hard on yourself. It simply means accepting that you made a mistake and that you are accountable for your actions.
- **Be honest with yourself** – Don't try to sugarcoat what you did or make excuses.
- **Self-reflection** – Engage in introspection to gain

insight into your own experiences, behaviors, and patterns related to addiction. This self-awareness will help you approach re-connection with a clearer understanding of yourself and your impact on others.

- **Feel your emotions** – Allow yourself to really feel the emotions that come up when you think about your mistakes. Don't try to suppress them or push them away. Perhaps write them down so that you have a list of what to work on. It's okay to feel sad, angry or frustrated.
- **Express remorse** – After you have taken responsibility for your mistake, it's important to acknowledge the remorse that you feel about your actions. This may mean telling another person what you are sorry for, but it can also just mean knowing within yourself that you are sorry for what you did and that you understand how your actions affected others.
- **Show yourself compassion** – Addiction is a difficult journey. It's easy to be hard on yourself, but remember that you're not alone, you're not perfect, and everyone makes mistakes. Forgive yourself for your past and focus on moving forward. Be kind to yourself and talk to yourself the way you would talk

to a friend.

- **Be willing to accept the consequences of your actions** – This may mean facing things like rejection, criticism, legal problems, health problems or discipline. It can be a difficult process, but by acknowledging your mistakes and facing the consequences, you can begin to rebuild your life and move on from your addiction. If possible, try to take just one problem at a time, as if it were a project you need to get done.
- **Learn from your mistakes** – It is *imperative* to learn from your mistakes. This means understanding why you made the mistake in the first place and what you can do to avoid making the same error in the future. No need to dwell on them, but learn from them and use them as an opportunity to grow and improve.
- **Move on** – Once you have forgiven yourself, it is important to move on. Don't dwell on the past. Focus on the present moment and your recovery.

JENNA'S TAKE

"Cutting out harmful relationships, then almost all relationships, was a process. Then I could choose who to let back in. Changing my own harmful behavior and continuing to catch myself when I fall short is a continuous practice in humility. And self-forgiveness! I had to get used to apologizing often and being sincere about it.

Truth is, the people who care about me and appreciate the efforts I'm making are more accepting and forgiving than I could have hoped. I think our worst critics and our worst enemies are ourselves. If you don't put yourself out there, make yourself vulnerable, you will never feel the amazing healing power that forgiveness and acceptance can bring.

Though a good outcome with every relationship is never a sure thing, you can still get some personal healing by doing what feels right on your end. You can only do your best and continue to strive to evolve. If you can't save an old relationship, allow yourself to move on and start a new one with someone else. Another couple of quotes I really like are, "A stranger is just a friend you haven't met yet," and, "We get to choose who our family is!"

THE CHALLENGES OF MENDING RELATIONSHIPS

The following may seem like just a list of bad behavior, but there's a purpose to it. Before you can mend any relationship, you need to know and think about how your addiction might have affected each person that you want to reconnect with.

As you read these lists, note which ones apply to your own various relationships (again, we recommend using "The Other Twelve Steps Workbook" to help you keep track):

- **Romantic Relationships**: Addiction can be really tough on romantic relationships. Before your newfound sobriety, your partner may have felt a range of emotions, including resentment, hurt, neglect, betrayal, anger and emotional exhaustion. They may have felt like they were walking on eggshells all the time, trying not to say or do anything that might trigger you back into using. There are many ways that romantic relationships can be affected by addiction:
- **Financial** – Because addiction is expensive, your partner may have been left to pick up the financial slack, leading to resentment and financial hardship.

- **Uncertainty** – When addiction causes unpredictable behavior in a partner, it can be difficult to feel connected. Instead of seeing you as the consistent, dependable person they once knew, they feel like they're dealing with a stranger who is always on the edge of a crisis.
- **Lack of intimacy** – If, at times, you were too preoccupied with your addiction to be interested in sex or even a nice cuddle, your partner may have felt lonely or isolated.
- **Trust issues** – Fear of being lied to can erode trust in a relationship. Your partner may have worried that you would relapse or lie to them about your addiction, which could have made it difficult for them to feel close to you, perhaps leading to arguments and conflict.
- **Communication problems** – Addiction can make it difficult for couples to communicate effectively. You may have been defensive or closed off, and your partner may have felt like they were treading on thin ice all the time. These kinds of feelings can make it difficult to resolve problems and may lead to feelings of frustration, hurt and hopelessness.

- **Family Relationships**: Addiction can have a devastating impact on your close or even extended family. Untreated addiction can eventually lead to the breakdown of the family, so you may be dealing with family turmoil in your recovery. Some common effects of addiction on family relationships are:
    - **Emotional distance** - Addiction can cause an emotional chasm between family members. You may have withdrawn from your loved ones and become isolated, making it difficult for them to feel close to you and leading to feelings of loneliness and abandonment on both sides.
    - **Lack of Trust** – During your struggle with addiction, it is possible that you resorted to deception or theft from your own family members to support your drug habit. It may be a major understatement to say that the aftermath of such actions likely led to a profound erosion of trust within the family.

JENNA'S TAKE

Though a good outcome with every relationship is never a sure thing, you can still get some personal healing by doing what feels right on your end. You can only do your best and continue to strive to evolve. If you can't save an old relationship, allow yourself to move on and start a new one with someone else. Another couple of quotes I really like are, "A stranger is just a friend you haven't met yet," and, "We get to choose who our family is!"

When trust is compromised among family members, it becomes difficult to foster a sense of closeness or connection, and open and honest communication becomes hindered at best and impossible at worst.

- **Financial strain** - The cost of drugs or alcohol may have put a lot of strain on your family finances, leading to hurtful words, arguments, stress or even bankruptcy.
- **Neglect of responsibilities** - Before you became sober, you may have neglected important responsibilities at home. Maybe you failed to help with household chores, bills or financial assistance, or in your role, helping care for children or aging parents. This could have led to

tension or resentment and may have strained your ties to other family members.

- **Violence -** During active addiction, you may have used violence to express your anger, frustration or pain. Or it may have been a way for you to control or manipulate others. Such violence may have been directed at yourself, your family or even strangers.
- **Child neglect or abuse** - If a parent is addicted to drugs or alcohol, they may neglect or abuse their children. This can have a lasting impact on the children's physical, emotional and mental health.
- **Shame and stigma** - Addiction can be a very isolating experience. You may have felt ashamed and embarrassed about your addiction and may have withdrawn from your family and friends, leading to feelings of loneliness and despair.
- **Friendships can suffer greatly due to addiction**. You may have been unreliable, canceling plans at the last minute or not showing up for events. These kinds of behaviors could have led to your friends feeling hurt, angry or disappointed. And unfortunately, your untreated addiction may have

eventually led to the loss of many precious friendships. Here are some ways that your friendships may have been affected:

- **Isolation** – As you struggled with addiction, you may have ignored your old friends and chosen to spend time with other addicts instead. This may have led to feelings of loneliness and isolation.

> ***JENNA'S TAKE***
>
> *"Truth is, the people who care about me and appreciate the efforts I'm making are more accepting and forgiving than I could have hoped. I think our worst critics and our worst enemies are ourselves. If you don't put yourself out there, make yourself vulnerable, you will never feel the amazing healing power that forgiveness and acceptance can bring.*

- **Lying and deception** – You may have lied to your friends about your drug use or made excuses for your behavior, trying to hide the extent of your addiction. This kind of deception likely made it difficult for your friends to trust you.
- **Professional Relationships can also be damaged by addiction**. You may have missed work or made mistakes. You might have become irresponsible, not meeting deadlines or not

following through on commitments. This may have led to co-workers feeling frustrated, angry and resentful, and your untreated addiction may have eventually led to the loss of your job.

Here are some of the effects your addiction may have had on your work life:

- **Increased absenteeism** – Addiction may have led to you missing too much work because you were too hungover or sick to go. You might also have been using alcohol to cope with stress or anxiety, leading you to call in sick more often.
- **Reduced productivity** – Your addiction may have also led to reduced productivity at work. Because you were struggling with addiction, you might have been less focused, less able to concentrate and more likely to make mistakes.
- **Increased accidents** – Addiction could have led to an increased risk of accidents at your workplace. People who are struggling with addiction are more likely to be impaired while at work, more likely to take risks that they would not normally take, and lack the focus or attention needed for the job.
- **Damaged relationships** – Addiction may have damaged some of your relationships at work because

you were irritable, aggressive or unreliable. In your addiction, you may also, at times, have had 'no filters,' making you more likely to gossip or spread rumors about your colleagues.

- **Loss of job** – In some cases, addiction leads to the loss of a job; employers may not be willing to tolerate the effects of impairment on an employee's performance and behavior.

Whew! What an exhausting list, no? But don't worry! This is where the good stuff starts – learning how to heal those (hopefully not) lost relationships!

So, now you know who you want to reconnect with and what mistakes you want to make amends for. Next, you'll want to arm yourself with good communication skills for your ultimate goal of reconciliation.

TIPS FOR COMMUNICATING EFFECTIVELY

This is important for three main reasons. First, it can help you to avoid misunderstandings and hurt feelings. Second, it can help you to manage conflict and come to solutions that work for everyone involved. Third, it can help you to build trust, which is essential in any relationship. Here are some tips to help you learn to communicate effectively:

- **Build trust** – This is essential in any relationship. When you communicate, show that you are interested in honesty, openness, mutual understanding and vulnerability – all of which are great building blocks for any relationship.
- **Be direct but polite** – Use "I" statements, like "I felt hurt when you did X," rather than blaming or accusing the other person.
- **Listen to understand, rather than listening to respond.** Pause before you respond. It's okay to say, "I need a minute to process what you said." This gives you time to avoid speaking in anger.
- **Stay positive**. This doesn't mean ignoring the hurt you may be feeling, but trying to use compassionate and positive language.
- **Respect each other**. Even when you disagree, treat the other person with kindness and consideration.

WHAT'S THE DIFFERENCE??

Negative Language is judgmental and critical. It focuses on the person's mistakes and failures. It uses harsh words and phrases that can make the person feel bad about themselves.

Compassionate and Positive Language is understanding and supportive. It focuses on the person's positive efforts and potential. It uses kind words and phrases that can help the person feel good about themselves.

COMMUNICATION TOOLS FOR CONFLICT RESOLUTION

Communication tools are a valuable resource for resolving conflict. They can help people to communicate more effectively, understand each other's point of view and find mutually beneficial solutions.

Active listening – This is a communication technique that involves paying attention to what the other person is saying, both verbally and non-verbally. It also involves reflecting back on what you have heard to ensure that you understand the other person's point of view.

IMPLEMENTING ACTIVE LISTENING

Person 1: I'm really stressed out about this project. What if I can't get it done on time?

Person 2: It sounds like you're feeling overwhelmed. Tell me more about what's stressing you out.

Person 1: I have a lot of other work to do, so I'm not sure how I'm going to fit this project in.

Person 2: I see. So, you're feeling like you don't have enough time to complete the project.

Person 1: Yes, and I'm worried that if I don't get it done, I'm going to get in trouble.

Person 2: I understand. That sounds like a lot of pressure.

In this example, Person 2 is using active listening skills to show that they are paying attention to Person 1 and trying to understand their point of view. They are also using open-ended questions to encourage Person 1 to share more information.

Assertive communication – This is a communication style that allows you to express your needs and wants clearly and directly without being aggressive or passive.

IMPLEMENTING ASSERTIVE COMMUNICATION

Your friend asks you to go out to an event on a Friday night, but you have too much work to do.

You could say: "I'm sorry, I can't go out tonight. I have a lot of work to do."

But this is a passive response. It is polite, but it does not express your needs or wants.

A more assertive response would be: "I would love to go out with you, but I have a lot of work to do tonight. Can we do something on Saturday instead?"

This response is assertive because it expresses your needs and wants clearly and directly. It is also polite and respectful of your friend's feelings.

- **Use "I" Statements** - "I" statements can help you to resolve conflicts and improve your relationships. "I" statements can be a helpful tool for communicating your feelings and needs in a clear, direct and courteous way.
- **Be specific** – When you are expressing your needs and wants, be as specific as possible. This will help the other person to understand what you need and how they can help you. For example, instead of saying, "I need help," you could say, "I need help with my homework."

USING "I" STATEMENTS

"I" statements are a good way to express your needs and wants without blaming or attacking the other person. For example, instead of saying, "You always make me feel like

I'm not good enough," you could say, "I feel like I'm not good enough when you say things like that."

Here is an example of using an "I" statement:

Your roommate is always leaving their dirty dishes in the sink. You are starting to feel frustrated and annoyed.

You could say: "I feel frustrated when I see dirty dishes in the sink. I would appreciate it if you would wash them after you use them."

This is an "I" statement because it expresses your feelings and needs without blaming or attacking your roommate. It is also specific because it tells your roommate exactly what you would like them to do.

OK! Ready to start reconnecting?

In recovery, it is important to reconnect with the people you may have hurt or alienated. Although this can be a difficult process, it is vital for your recovery and for your relationships. Don't let the prospect of doing this overwhelm you. Just like paying down your credit card 'smallest one first,' start by reaching out to people who you think are most likely to be receptive to your apology. These might be people who you were close to before your addiction, or people who have expressed support for your recovery.

When you reconnect with people, you give them the opportunity to forgive you and to move on, too! You also show that you are really committed to your recovery. Reconnecting with your friends and loved ones not only helps you rebuild the trust that may have been lost when you were in active addiction, it also provides you with the support and accountability you need to stay sober. As you reconnect with friends and family, they can help you to stay on your recovery path and be there to celebrate your accomplishments. Your number ONE job here? Stay Trustworthy!

Here are some other important steps to remember in your re-connection journey:

- **Be respectful**: Even when you are assertive, it is important to be respectful of the other person's feelings. Remember that you are both trying to get your needs met.
- **Empathize:** Try and put yourself in their shoes and see the situation from their point of view.
- **Apologize:** Take responsibility for your past actions and make sincere apologies to those you have hurt or affected during your addiction.

- **Be willing to listen to the other person's feelings**. They may be angry, hurt or disappointed in you. It is important to let them express their feelings and to listen without judgment.
- **Be patient.** It may take time for the other person to forgive you and to rebuild trust. Be patient and understanding, and continue to show them that you are absolutely committed to your recovery.
- **Make amends:** Make amends where you can by taking concrete steps to rectify any harm caused, demonstrating your commitment to change.
- **Be prepared to answer questions about your addiction and your recovery**. People who have been hurt by your addiction may want to know why you used, how you got sober, and what you are doing to stay sober.
- **Rebuild trust gradually.** Understand that rebuilding trust takes time and consistency. Be patient and consistent in your actions, demonstrating reliability, honesty and accountability. Allow others to observe your sustained commitment to your recovery and personal growth.

- **Don’t give up hope!** As long as you are committed to honesty, growth and change, there's always hope for reconnecting and repairing relationships.

As you navigate the twists and turns of this reconciliation process and encounter more challenging situations, you can try out these additional techniques to help you stay on track:

- **Problem-solving**: A means of working with the other person to find a solution that meets the needs of both parties.
- **Mediation**: A way that a neutral third party can help the two parties to resolve their conflict.
- **Negotiation**: A process in which the two parties bargain with each other to reach an agreement.

Maintaining healthy relationships is an important part of addiction recovery. Forgiving yourself and others, communicating openly, and rebuilding trust will help you create a strong support network. Be patient and kind to yourself as you take these steps. A solid social life will be a pillar of your sobriety!

As you progress in your recovery, it's important to celebrate each small victory. Every time you do something positive, like connecting with an old friend or resisting a temptation to use, you are making strides in your recovery journey. Every little win is a sign that your hard work is paying off, and it can motivate you to keep going. Celebrating your wins is also important for the people in your life who are choosing to support you through recovery!

CHAPTER 7 RESOURCES

SELF-FORGIVENESS

- **Put The Shovel Down video**: Self-Forgiveness (even if you don't deserve it).
- **Stabilis Treatment Centre video**: 4 Steps to Self-Forgiveness in Recovery
- **TheMeadows.com article**: 5 Ways to Practice Self-Forgiveness in Recovery
- **WhatCheriThinks.com article**: 8 Self-Forgiveness Exercises and Techniques That Really Work

MENDING RELATIONSHIPS

- **Tracy Struckman video**: Guide to Healing Relationships After Addiction
- **TheDawnRehab.com article**: On the Mend: How to Repair Broken Relationships After Addiction
- **AddictionCenter.com article**: How Do I Regain My Loved Ones' Trust After Rehab?
- **Health.USNews.com article**: Making Successful Amends After Addiction: Keys to Repairing Relationships

COMMUNICATION SKILLS:

- **Fostering Resilience video**: How to Improve Your Communication Skills in Early Recovery
- **TED-Ed video**: The Best Way to Apologize (According to Science)
- **Buckeye Recovery Network video**: 6 Keys for Effective Communication
- **DrPaulByTheSea.com article**: 5 Communications Skills for Recovery

LEARNING ASSERTIVENESS:

- **NorthStarTransitions.com article**: Eight Ways to Practice Assertive Communication in Recovery
- **DesertHopeTreatment.com article**: Are You a Doormat in Recovery? How to Be More Assertive Now
- **Ceilli Rose video**: Assertive Communication Video (this is a fun one!)

MAKING AMENDS:

- **Michelle Farris, Relationship Therapist video**: How to Make Amends: 7 Tips that Work

- **NewStartRecovery.com article**: Do's and Don'ts: Examples of Making Amends in Recovery
- **HazeldenBettyFord.org article**: Making Amends in Addiction Recovery

CHAPTER 8
It Feels Good to Look Good!

When you're deep into active addiction, the last thing you're thinking about is whether your hair looks good or your clothes (or even your shoes!) match. You're in survival mode and looking good is just not a priority. However, once you're in recovery, taking care of yourself becomes important again, and it can be a way to feel good about yourself and your new life.

Of course, you don't have to be super-fancy or dress like you're going to the Oscars – we're not talking about getting all glammed up here. But taking a little time each morning to put yourself together can give you a lift and make you feel more put-together, both physically and mentally. And when you feel good, it shows!

JENNA'S TAKE

"Self-care is one thing. But how you see yourself is different. During my addiction I stopped caring about a lot of things, such as how I looked or smelled, what I ate, and where I slept. I could see the dysfunction and felt disappointed in myself when I looked in the mirror. But at the time I felt I deserved to feel that way, almost like self-punishment.

So, after working on getting sober then getting healthier, I wanted and needed that to reflect back at me when I saw myself. It was a slow start – there was a lot of dirt to wipe away. But eventually I uncovered the beautiful person I remembered. So now to do myself up and be proud of where I am is like a reward. It reminds me of the work I've done. It gives me a boost of confidence. If I'm going out to do something important, the process of getting clean refreshes my soul and resets my mind. Grooming myself with love and putting on a little shine or sparkle to let the world know I am beautiful inside and out just feels good. And if I'm in a rut, it lifts me up. I am worth it. YOU are worth it! You deserve to look and feel great!"

CREATE A MORNING RITUAL

A morning hygiene ritual can set the tone for your entire day. It's a time to wake up your body and mind and prepare for the day ahead. Brushing your teeth, showering or bathing and taking care of your hair and face are all ways to feel fresh and clean and ready to take on the day. Also, taking a moment to pause and just breathe can help you feel grounded and ready to start your day on the right foot.

There are so many ways to create a morning ritual that feels good to you! Aside from personal hygiene, it can include things like stretching, meditation, prayer or setting intentions for the day. What it should not include is scrolling through emails and social media! Save that for later in the day. Having a morning routine that you enjoy can set you up for a pleasant and productive day and can be very helpful for keeping yourself on track, especially in early sobriety.

GROOMING FOR SUCCESS!

Grooming, in the context of personal appearance, means the act of cleaning and taking care of your hair, skin and nails. Think of your morning grooming as a process of self-care, which can include things like:

- Washing, brushing and styling your hair
- Brushing and flossing your teeth
- Shaving or trimming your beard
- Putting on any makeup you like
- Applying products like lotion, makeup, hair products, deodorant or fragrance
- Making sure your nails are clean and respectable

In addition to making you look presentable, grooming can also be a way to express yourself and to look and feel your best. This kind of habit can help set the tone for your whole day, so try to get up early enough to be able to enjoy the process and feel good about yourself!

EMBRACE THE POWER OF A GOOD HAIR DAY

We've all done it. We've all had the awesome feeling of a Good Hair Day. They are so rare and precious! The exhilaration of knowing that you look *'Goooooood'* is so much fun to experience! It may seem like a small thing, but getting a haircut or style that you love can be a symbolic gesture of making a positive change, a sign to yourself and the people around you that you're serious about recovery.

We've all, of course, also experienced the bedhead blues. When your hair is a mess in the morning, it can make you feel less than your best and can affect your mood and productivity for the whole day. But taking the time to style your hair in a way that makes you feel confident and put together can give you a mental and emotional boost that carries you through the day. When you feel good about yourself, it shows in your appearance and can help you project the best version of yourself to the world.

When you were struggling with addiction, taking care of your appearance and your overall health may have been the last thing on your mind. After all, when you were focused on feeding the addiction, how you looked and felt probably took a back seat most of the time. But as you move into recovery and start to get your life back on track, you may find that a new cut or style can be a powerful symbolic gesture and a visual reminder of your transformation.

And don't worry – if your wallet's a bit skint at the moment, there are ways to get started for little to nothing. Maybe your local cosmetology school is looking for willing hair models. Or you can ask your local community referral service if any other organizations can give you a hand up in your pursuit of getting ready for a job interview.

Taking the time to focus on your appearance can be a powerful form of self-care in early sobriety. When you look good, you feel good! A fresh haircut and a well-chosen outfit can give you the confidence you need to face your day with strength and positivity. Even on a rough day, looking good can be a reminder that you are worth it and deserve all the good things life has to offer. So go ahead and take care of yourself – you deserve it!

DRESS TO *FEEL* YOUR BEST

The way you dress can also have a big impact on how you feel about yourself. If you take the time to get dressed with intention, it can make a big difference in your confidence and mood for the day.

Dressing in clothes that fit well and are comfortable can give you a sense of confidence and self-assurance. This means clothing that is not too tight or revealing but also not too loose or baggy. Just comfortable. Not sure where to start? Pinterest is a great source of style inspiration!

Feeling your best can give you the energy and strength to tackle whatever comes your way. Taking the time to choose clothes that are in good condition and that look sharp can be like putting on your superhero cape. It can give you that "you can do it!" attitude and inspire you to be your best self. Paying attention to small details like your shoes, your accessories and your hairstyle can also add an extra boost.

Color is another factor to think about when dressing for your day. Choosing your colors carefully can be an easy way to improve your mood. Bright colors can lift your spirits when you're feeling down, and soft colors can calm you when you're feeling overwhelmed.

If you're going out, dress for the occasion, whether that's overalls to go pick apples, casual to go to the grocery store or your tucked-up black best for an evening event. Wherever you're going, dressing with intention will help you feel your best. That means taking the time to think about what you're wearing and why. It's about being mindful and deliberate in your clothing choices rather than just grabbing whatever is clean or nearby. Dressing with intention can be as simple as asking yourself, "How do I want to feel today?" and choosing your clothes accordingly. It's about making choices that help you feel good and that align with your goals and values.

If you've got a big interview coming up, or you've lost your job to addiction, and you're trying to get back on your feet, dressing your best can also give your self-esteem a much-needed boost. All of these things are small but important steps toward taking control of your life again. Even if you've had a rough time, you can show up looking sharp and feeling ready for whatever comes next!

"But," you may say, "I don't have any clothes good enough for a job interview!" Well, you're in luck, my friend, because many non-profit organizations specialize in providing good quality clothing and shoes to folks who are making their way back into the working world, such as:

- Dress for Success
- Altrusa Women's Wardrobe
- Career Gear (for men)
- WorkingWardrobes.org
- The Junior League
- Soroptimist International's Career Closet

- Soles4Souls

These and many others around the world serve different subsets of people (women, men, people coming out of abusive situations, trafficked people, folks coming out of prison, people in recovery, etc.). So, call your local community referral service or ask your doctor or therapist for information on what is available in your area.

In most of the United States, you can call 211, which will hook you up with local referral specialists. Tell them your circumstances and that you are re-entering the job market. If there are non-profits in your area that provide clothing or haircuts for people in situations like yours, they will be able to give you contact information.

You might be surprised how much your appearance affects your mood, attitude and motivation. Looking good can have a very positive impact on you in the early stages of addiction recovery in so many ways! It can:

- **Boost your self-esteem:** When you take the time to look your best, it can help you feel more confident and positive about yourself. This can be especially important for you in early recovery while you may be struggling with low self-esteem as a result of your addiction.

- **Improve your mood:** Feeling good about your appearance can also lead to feeling happier. When you feel good about how you look, you're more likely to feel positive and optimistic about yourself and your future. This can be a helpful boost during the challenging early stages of recovery.
- **Increase your motivation:** When you feel good about yourself, you're more likely to be motivated to take positive steps in your life, such as attending treatment, working on your sobriety and rebuilding your relationships.
- **Attract positive attention:** Looking good can also help you attract positive attention from others. This can be helpful in recovery, as it can provide you with the support and encouragement you need to stay on track.

While there are many elements to a successful recovery from addiction, taking care of your appearance is certainly a valuable part of the process. It's not the only factor, but it can be a helpful support along the way. Making an effort to look your best can boost your self-esteem and give you the motivation you need to keep on the path to recovery. And it can have a positive effect on the people around you as well, helping to create a much-needed sense of support and understanding in your community!

HELPFUL TIP

Do an internet search for "your city name + career clothing donations" to find organizations near you that can help.

CHAPTER 8 RESOURCES

DRESS TO FEEL YOUR BEST

- **Self.com article:** How to Embrace 'Dopamine Dressing' and Shop Your Own Closet
- **TheGuardian.com article:** How to Dress Yourself Happy, One Feelgood Outfit at a Time

HAVE A GOOD HAIR DAY

- **McShin Foundation video**: Thanks, Charlie - A haircut can change everything
- **Calgary.ctvnews.ca article**: Fresh Cuts a 'Fresh Start' for Recovering Addicts
- **DealTrunk.com**: Ideas for ways to get free haircuts, no matter where you live.
- Also, try doing an internet search for "free haircuts for those in need."

PERSONAL HYGIENE IN RECOVERY

- **MoreThanRehab.com article:** Hygiene and Drug Use: Why Does Use Cause a Lack of Care?
- **HannahsHouse.com article:** What is Self-Care in Addiction Recovery and How Do You Practice It?

- **MedicalNewsToday.com article: Why** is personal hygiene important?

INTERNATIONAL RESOURCES

- **Soles4Souls.org:** These folks partner with non-profit organizations around the world to provide new shoes to those who need them most.

- **OneWarmCoat.org:** Partners with non-profit agencies and schools in communities across all 50 states to distribute coats for free to children and adults in need.
- **DressForSuccess.org:** Mission: To empower women to achieve economic independence by providing a network of support, professional attire and development tools to help women thrive in work and in life.

- **JailsToJobs.org:** Has a directory of nonprofits across the U.S. that are dedicated to giving away professional clothing to those who qualify.
- **The Wardrobe Box:** "The Wardrobe Box allows people all across the country to conveniently receive our services where they are."

Also, try doing an internet search for "free clothing for those in need."

CHAPTER 9
Take Care of the Legal Stuff

Just as it's important to get your finances and paperwork in order in early sobriety, dealing with the legal consequences of your past actions is a critical step in moving forward. There may be a number of outstanding legal issues that need to be resolved, and the process can feel daunting. But it's important to face these challenges head-on and take steps to settle them so that you can focus on your recovery without the weight of legal matters hanging over your head. Of course, every person's story is different, and the best approach will vary depending on your circumstances.

IMPORTANT NOTE

This chapter is not intended to provide legal advice or a specific solution for any legal problems you may be facing. Rather, it's meant to offer general guidance and information about how to approach the legal system with the best attitude and strategies.

There are so many things that you could be dealing with. Just think what a relief it will be when outstanding warrants, court cases, fines and any other legal consequences are taken care of, and you can truly move forward! It's crucial to get all your legal matters resolved as part of the process of moving on from addiction and building your new life. It will help you to gain a sense of closure and feel like you are truly getting a fresh start!

Every person's legal situation is different, and you may need to seek help from a lawyer or legal professional to deal with your specific circumstances. Hopefully, this chapter can help you get started in the right direction and set you on the path to resolving any legal challenges in your life.

UNDERSTAND YOUR LEGAL RIGHTS

As a newly sober person, you may have legal rights that you are not aware of. For example, you may be entitled to a public defender if you are arrested, or you may be able to have your criminal record expunged if you complete a drug treatment program. It is important to understand your legal rights so that you can protect yourself, so ask your attorney.

UNDERSTAND YOUR LEGAL RESPONSIBILITIES

It's important to understand your legal responsibilities as well. Knowing what the law requires of you can help you stay on the right track and avoid further legal trouble. Depending on your situation, this might mean understanding your probation terms, any restitution requirements or any court-mandated treatment, educational programs or fines.

GET HELP WITH LEGAL PROBLEMS

When you have legal troubles, such as a criminal charge or a child custody dispute, it is essential to get help. There are many resources available to help you, such as free legal aid clinics, lawyers who specialize in addiction law and support groups for people with legal problems.

BE HONEST WITH YOUR LAWYER

Your lawyer is there to help you, but they can only do that if you are honest with them. Tell your lawyer everything about your addiction and your legal problems.

BE COOPERATIVE WITH THE COURT SYSTEM

- The odds of leniency may increase in your favor if you are cooperative.
- Be respectful and courteous.
- Dress well. (See Chapter 8 for info on where to get appropriate clothing)
- Show up for all of your court dates, even if they are just phone-ins.
- Follow the orders of the court and pay your fines.

JENNA'S TAKE

"Being a 'rebel without a cause' was great when I was younger. But that kind of behavior starts to build a hard crust, like barnacles on the bottom of a boat. You can't see them from the surface, but they are getting thicker and heavier every day, creating drag in the water. It seemed easier for me for a long time to just keep running. Keep moving. But always moving kept me from ever being grounded or being a real part of my community. It's a lonely life.

The thought of staying put and taking my lashes, of course, was not very attractive. But once I tore that band-aid off things did start to improve for me. People wanted to help me do better. They weren't hoping for me to fail or waiting to see me fall on my face, as I had imagined. Also, to get all of it on paper in front of me and talk to a lawyer that could help me understand was a ***huge*** *weight off. I had been making it way harder in my imagination. I had a court appointed lawyer and all they wanted me to do was.... Show UP! And show up again!!*

I learned that doing the right thing can be a reward in itself. Now I feel safe staying in one place, building on my family and relationships and self without living in a constant state of fear. The law is not perfect, but it is better to be on their good side at this point. Make that leap!"

STAY POSITIVE

When facing legal challenges and the consequences of past actions, it can be easy to get overwhelmed and discouraged. But staying positive is vital as you go through this process. Try to remember that you are on the path to a better life, even if the road is bumpy at times. Positivity will help you see things from a more hopeful perspective and keep you motivated even if the going gets a bit rough.

ASK QUESTIONS

As mentioned earlier, you may have legal rights that you are not aware of. Keep a small notepad handy so that you can jot down any and all questions that pop into your head. Then, you can address them with your attorney at your next meeting or on your next phone call.

FINANCES

If you need help with paying your fines, ask your attorney for assistance with the issue. They may know if a payment plan is available. Remember to be assertive (not aggressive), clear and direct about what you need.

STAY ORGANIZED!!

- If you are entitled to them, ask for copies of all documents pertaining to your case(s) and keep them organized in your files at home.
- Use a calendar to stay on top of appearance dates and appointments with your lawyer so that you don't miss any of them, even the phone-ins.
- Dedicate a specific notepad to this project. Take good notes not only when you are in a legal setting, a courtroom or a meeting with your attorney, but also whenever you are on a phone call about the matter.
- If you are dealing with more than one case, have a separate notepad for each one.
- Use the first couple of pages of the notepads for important phone numbers and addresses pertaining to each case.

DEFINITIONS

Going to Court: Who is involved?

- **Plaintiff:** Also called the "prosecution," this is the person or entity who is filing the case, bringing a charge against another person or entity. The plaintiff has the burden of proof, which means they have to provide evidence that their accusation is true.

- **Defendant:** The person who is being accused of doing something wrong and who is defending against the charge. The defendant has the right to remain silent and doesn't have to prove their innocence.
- **Attorney:** Someone who has passed the bar exam and has been admitted to practice law.
- **Lawyer:** A general term that refers to anyone who has studied law.
- **Judge:** A person who presides over court cases and makes decisions about the law.
- **Jury:** A group of people who listen to the evidence and decide the outcome of a case.
- **Grand Jury:** A group of citizens who are tasked with deciding whether there is enough evidence to charge someone with a crime. If the grand jury finds that there is probable cause to believe that the defendant committed the crime, they will issue an indictment. The indictment will then be served on the defendant, who will be arraigned on the charges.

Going to Court: Types of Court Proceedings/Filings

- **Complaint*:*** A document that is filed by the prosecution with the court to initiate a criminal case. The complaint will allege that the defendant has committed a crime, but it will not be a formal accusation. The grand jury will decide whether to issue an indictment after reviewing the evidence in the case.
- **Arraignment*:*** At arraignment, the defendant is advised of the charges against them, enters a plea of guilty or not guilty, and is informed of their rights. The defendant is also allowed to request a jury trial.

Hearings

- **Pre-Trial Hearings** are used to discuss issues like discovery (sharing evidence between the parties), motions (requests to the court for certain actions), and jury selection.
- **Preliminary Hearing:** At a preliminary hearing, the prosecution presents evidence to the judge to determine if there is enough evidence to hold the defendant over for trial.
- **Summary judgment hearings** are held to determine whether the case can be decided without a trial.

- **Sentencing Hearings** are when the defendant is told their punishment.
- **Indictment*:*** A formal accusation of a crime issued by a grand jury.
- **Trial*:*** At trial, the prosecution and defense present evidence to the judge or jury. The judge or jury will then decide whether the defendant is guilty or not guilty based on the evidence that was presented. If the defendant is found guilty, the judge or jury will decide on a sentence.
- **Sentencing*:*** Sentencing is the final step in a criminal case. The judge will sentence the defendant to a punishment, such as jail time, probation or a fine. The length of the sentence will depend on the severity of the crime.
- **Appeal:** An appeal is a process by which a higher court reviews the decision of a lower court to determine if it is correct. The defendant must file a notice of appeal with the higher court within a certain amount of time after the lower court's decision. The higher court will then review the record of the case and may hold a hearing to hear arguments from the parties. After the review, the higher court will issue a decision which may affirm the lower court's decision,

reverse the lower court's decision, or remand the case back to the lower court for further proceedings.

Going to Court: Types of Crimes

- **Felony***:* A serious crime that is punishable by more than one year in prison. Felonies are typically divided into two categories: violent felonies and property crimes. Some examples of felonies are Murder, Rape, Robbery, Assault, Burglary, Theft and Arson.
- **Misdemeanor:** A crime that is considered to be less serious than a felony. Misdemeanors are typically punishable by less than one year in jail, a fine, or both. Some common examples of misdemeanors are Disorderly Conduct, Simple Assault, Theft, Public Intoxication and Vandalism.

Going to Court: Other Legal Processes

- **Bail:** A sum of money that is paid to the court to secure the release of a defendant from jail pending trial. The defendant promises to appear in court for all scheduled court dates and to pay the bail amount if they fail to appear. If the defendant appears in court as promised, the bail money is returned.

- **Bond:** A type of loan that is secured by the defendant's property. The bond amount is typically 10% of the bail amount. If the defendant fails to appear in court, the bond company will forfeit the bond amount to the court.
- **Expungement:** A process that allows a person to have their criminal record sealed or erased, depending on the situation.
- **Injunction**: A court order that requires a person or organization to do (or not do) something. It's like a legal command that tells someone to stop a specific behavior or start doing something differently. Injunctions are often used in cases where someone is causing harm or violating the rights of others, and the court wants to put a stop to it.
- **Parole:** A conditional release from prison that allows an individual to serve the remainder of their sentence outside of the prison system. The individual must abide by conditions such as check-ins with a parole officer, regular drug testing and staying away from known criminals.
- **Probation:** A type of community supervision that is used as an alternative to incarceration. Typically ordered by a judge as part of a sentence, the offender

must comply with certain conditions, such as reporting to a probation officer, completing community service hours, and abstaining from drugs and alcohol.

- **Plea Bargain:** An agreement between the defendant and the prosecutor where the defendant agrees to plead guilty in exchange for a reduced sentence.
- **Plea Deal:** An agreement between a prosecutor and a defendant in a criminal case. In a plea deal, the defendant agrees to plead guilty to a lesser charge or to certain counts of a multi-count indictment in exchange for a reduction in the charges or a more lenient sentence.
- **Pro Bono:** Legal services that are provided free of charge, usually to people who can't afford to pay for them.
- **Warrant:** A legal document issued by a court that allows law enforcement to arrest an individual or search a property. There are different types of warrants, including search warrants, arrest warrants, and bench warrants.

MAINTAIN YOUR DIGNITY

Sometimes, the process of navigating the legal system can be degrading or dehumanizing, and it's important to remember that you are still a person with value, no matter what the situation.

- ***Be kind to yourself.*** Remember that you are not defined by your mistakes, and you are capable of change and growth.
- ***Take care of your physical and mental health.*** Eat well, exercise, and try to get enough sleep. It can be hard to do those things when you're going through a difficult time, but they are essential for staying strong.
- ***Lean on your support system.*** Talk to your loved ones, your sponsor, or a therapist about how you're feeling. Don't try to go through this alone.

TAKE IT ONE STEP AT A TIME

Sometimes, the legal process can seem overwhelming and never-ending. It can be helpful to focus on one step at a time. It can be easy to get caught up in the big picture and lose sight of the day-to-day progress you're making, so try to stay grounded and focused on the task at hand.

CELEBRATE THE SMALL VICTORIES!

Showing up to court on time, filling out paperwork correctly, or successfully completing an assignment from the court can all be small victories that are worth celebrating. Even something as simple as getting a good night's sleep can feel like a victory in the midst of a difficult legal situation. So, try to recognize and celebrate these small wins, no matter how insignificant they may seem. It can help to keep you motivated and positive as you move through the legal process.

DON'T GIVE UP!

It's easy to feel overwhelmed and defeated when facing legal challenges in recovery. But please keep the following in mind: First, you are capable of change. You have already overcome so much in your journey to recovery, and you can overcome these challenges as well.

Second, you have support. Reach out to your loved ones, your sponsor or your therapist for help.

And third, there is a light at the end of the tunnel. The legal process can be slow and frustrating, but eventually, it will be over. Hang in there and stay focused on your goals and your future!

STAY SOBER!!

The most important thing you can do to protect yourself legally is to stay sober. When you are sober, you are less likely to make bad decisions that could lead to additional problems. You are also more likely to be able to work with your lawyer to resolve your legal problems positively.

GET HELP FROM A SUPPORT GROUP

While there may not be support groups that specifically deal with legal issues, there are many support groups that can help with the anxiety, stress, and other emotional consequences of having legal issues. These can include 12-step groups, church support groups, or counseling groups.

DIFFERENT TYPES OF LAW

This list is not meant to be exhaustive but to just provide an overview of the types of law that someone in addiction recovery may need to deal with.

Criminal Law: Criminal law covers a wide range of crimes, from minor offenses like petty theft to serious felonies like murder. Common crimes that fall under criminal law include assault, battery, drug offenses, theft, fraud, and sexual offenses. Less serious crimes, called misdemeanors, usually result in a fine or a short jail sentence.

More serious crimes, called felonies, can result in a long prison sentence or even the death penalty. Some criminal cases are heard in state court, while others are heard in federal court. This is determined by the type of crime and where it was committed.

Civil Law: Civil law covers a wide range of disputes between individuals, organizations, or businesses. Some common types of civil law cases include contract disputes, divorce and child custody issues, landlord-tenant disagreements, personal injury claims, and discrimination lawsuits. Civil law cases are typically resolved through monetary damages, injunctions, or other remedies rather than jail time.

In some cases, the court can order a specific action, such as requiring a landlord to make repairs to a rental property or forcing a business to stop discriminating against customers.

Family Law: Family law covers legal issues that involve family relationships, such as marriage, divorce, child custody, child support and adoption. These cases are typically handled in state court, but some may be heard in federal court if there are interstate issues, such as a divorce involving property located in multiple states. Family law cases can be very emotional and difficult to resolve, but they are often resolved through settlements or mediation rather than going to trial. If a case does go to trial, the court will consider what is in the best interests of the children involved, if any.

Immigration Law: Immigration law covers cases involving immigration and naturalization. This includes applications for visas, green cards, and citizenship, as well as deportation proceedings and asylum cases. Immigration law is a highly specialized area of law, and it is governed by both federal and state law.

In some cases, immigration law can intersect with other areas of law, such as criminal law or family law. For example, a person who has been convicted of a crime may be deported, or a person who has been separated from their spouse may need to adjust their immigration status.

CHAPTER 9 RESOURCES

Understand Your Rights and Responsibilities

- https://www.lawyers.com/legal-info/research/clients-bill-of-rights.html**Lawyers.com article**: Client's Bill of Rights When Dealing with Lawyers
- ***HG.org article*:** What To Expect from Your Attorney and What Your Attorney Expects from You

Know What Kind of Lawyer You Need

- ***RocketLawyer.com website:*** Provides a comprehensive list of types of law so that you can learn more about the specific type of lawyer that best fits your legal issue.
- ***LegalMatch.com article:*** An easy-to-understand overview of different types of lawyers
- ***LawSoup.org:*** A handy chart that shows issues on the left and the appropriate type of lawyer for that issue on the right.

Find Free (or low-cost) Legal Help

- ***LowIncomeRelief.com/Legal-Aid:*** Select your state from their list to see what free legal resources are available in your area.
- ***SoloSuit.com:*** "Get the help you need to navigate debt disputes. Their automated software will help you get resolution."
- ***LawHelp.org directory:*** LawHelp.org and state LawHelp sites are maintained by Pro Bono Net in partnership with dozens of nonprofit legal aid, pro bono, court-based programs and libraries across the country committed to access to justice.
- ***FreeLegalAnswers.org website:*** This is an American Bar Association website that lets you ask non-criminal law questions for free.

Find a Good Lawyer

- ***SuperLawyers.com website***: "Index of attorneys who practice quality and excellence in their work."
- ***NOLO.com article***: How to Find an Excellent Lawyer
- ***AmericanBar.org article***: How Do I Find a Lawyer?

- ***LawyersLegalLaws.com* website**: Online lead generator for finding the right lawyer.
- ***LegalMatch.com*:** "LegalMatch.com can connect you with an attorney who specializes in nearly any type of law practically anywhere in the country and does so in a timely manner."
- ***LegalZoom.com* directory:** Easy to use and provides reviews and good biographies.

CHAPTER 10
Give Back to the World

Volunteering in addiction recovery is a topic that interests many people who are looking for ways to help themselves overcome substance use disorders. One of the best ways to help YOU is to help others, and there are so many ways you can benefit from giving your time in volunteer efforts. It can:

- Help keep you occupied and focused on something positive, which can aid in preventing relapse
- Provide a sense of purpose and meaning, which is so vital in early sobriety.

- Help you rebuild your self-esteem and self-worth, which may have been damaged while you were in active addiction.
- Help you connect with a community of like-minded people who are also working to give back.

Volunteering can also have an array of other benefits for you as a recovering addict, such as:

- Reclaiming a sense of belonging that you may have lost while in the depths of addiction.
- Boosting your self-esteem and gaining a sense of purpose, all while giving to others.
- Forming social connections with new people and building relationships with both the people you are serving and the people you are serving alongside.
- Developing new skills and gaining valuable experience that can enhance your personal and professional life.
- Giving back to the community and supporting a cause that you care about.

In every community, and no matter what your circumstance, there are numerous ways to help out, even if your community is small or your capabilities are narrow. Everyone can contribute to making their community a better place.

JENNA'S TAKE

"I believe in fair trade, in pretty much all things. And I received a lot of help along my road to recovery. So, when is it time to give back to this wonderful, selfless community? Any time you feel ready. Any time you're feeling successful and energetic, share that love!

There are so many ways. I received free clothes, food and shelter, so these are some areas I'd like to give back, fulfilling my idea of fair trade, or passing it on. Love and understanding go a long way, too. Just going to meetings to share your story may fall on eager ears like mine as a newcomer, and then listening to the new person's story also may change their whole day, help their frustrations get released or feel not alone. Sometimes it's the smallest of efforts that make the biggest difference. Strangers, many strangers, did it for me. It makes me happy to return the favor."

Here is a list of volunteering ideas, depending on what you're interested in:

If you love animals, you could:

- Walk dogs at a local shelter
- Foster animals who are awaiting adoption.

- Transport animals to and from veterinary appointments or rescue facilities
- Socialize animals who are shy or fearful of people.
- Help with adoption events or community outreach efforts.
- Provide animal-assisted therapy to people in hospitals, nursing homes, or other settings.
- Care for animals in need at a wildlife rehabilitation center.
- Help with a spay/neuter clinic
- Provide pet therapy at a nursing home or school.

If you love forests, nature and being outdoors, you could:

- Plant trees or native plants in a park or other green space.
- Work on a local clean-up crew or river-monitoring team.
- Educate others about the importance of forests and nature.
- Take part in citizen science projects, such as monitoring bird populations or water quality.
- Support local land trusts or other organizations that work to protect forests and natural areas.

- Help with habitat restoration projects, such as removing invasive species or restoring wetlands.
- Help maintain hiking trails or parks in your area.
- Teach outdoor skills, such as camping, fishing, or orienteering.
- Lead nature hikes or bird-watching excursions.
- Help with habitat restoration projects.

If you have carpentry or construction skills, you could:

- Help to build or repair homes for low-income families or victims of natural disasters.
- Assist with Habitat for Humanity projects or other similar initiatives.
- Help with building or repairing community facilities, such as playgrounds, trails, or gardens.
- Build or install structures for local wildlife, such as bat houses or nesting boxes.
- Help with disaster relief efforts, such as rebuilding homes after a hurricane or tornado.
- Make repairs or renovations to nonprofit facilities, such as shelters or food banks.

If you enjoy working with children and teens, you could get involved by volunteering to:

- Coach a youth sports team.
- Tutor students in math, reading or other subjects.
- Help with an after-school program or summer camp.
- Volunteer at a library, museum, or other community organization that provides educational programs.
- Work with a Big Brothers Big Sisters program or other mentoring organization.
- Provide childcare for families in need.
- Facilitate recreational activities, such as art projects or music lessons.
- Volunteer at a school or after-school program.

If you are an art lover, you could get involved in your community by:

- Volunteering to teach art classes at a community center.
- Volunteering at a local museum or art gallery.
- Helping with an art therapy program for people with disabilities or illnesses.
- Teaching art classes or workshops.
- Creating art installations or murals in public spaces.
- Assisting with a community art project, such as a mural or sculpture.

- Making art kits or craft supplies for families in need.
- Donating art supplies to a school or community center.
- Hosting an art show or other fundraising event to support the arts.

If you love cooking, there are many ways you can share your passion with others:

- Volunteering at a soup kitchen or other community food program.
- Cooking for a senior center or retirement home.
- Creating and distributing meals to families in need.
- Teaching cooking classes or demonstrations.
- Making meals for people with disabilities or illnesses.
- Organizing a community potluck or other food-related event.
- Helping with food drives or other food collection efforts.
- Donating ingredients, kitchen supplies or time to a local food pantry.

If you love gardening, you could volunteer to:

- Create or help maintain a community garden.
- Teach gardening classes or workshops.

- Volunteer at a botanical garden or other community green space.
- Provide support for urban agriculture projects.
- Plant trees or other plants in public spaces.
- Make seed bombs or other projects to encourage native plant growth.
- Design and build rain gardens or other sustainable landscapes.
- Create and maintain school gardens or other educational gardens.
- Help to beautify a neighborhood or an apartment complex.

If you are a person who loves sports, you could volunteer:

- As a coach for a youth sports team.
- As a referee or umpire for a community sports league.
- As a scorekeeper or timer running the scoreboard or other equipment for a local sporting event.
- As a field marshal or equipment manager for a local sports club.
- To maintain fields or other facilities for local sports teams.
- As an announcer or DJ for a local sporting event.

- To work in a sports media department such as a local sports TV station or radio station.
- To help with ticket sales or fan support at a local sporting event.
- To serve as a team mascot or cheerleader.

If you love reading, you could volunteer:

- At a local library, reading to children, helping with events, programs or other activities.
- As a tutor or reading buddy for children or adults.
- To read to seniors in nursing homes or assisted living facilities.
- To record audio books for the blind or visually impaired.
- To work in a literacy program, helping people learn to read.

If you love music, you can volunteer in a variety of ways, including:

- Teaching music lessons or conducting an ensemble.
- Working in a community music center providing support and resources for musicians.
- Organizing or helping to run a local music festival or concert series.

- Performing music for seniors, hospital patients or other groups.
- Creating music playlists for nursing homes, hospitals or other facilities.
- Working with a music therapy program, providing therapeutic music experiences for people in need.
- Writing or producing a community radio show or podcast that features local bands.
- Making music videos for local musicians.
- Creating and distributing music-themed ezines or magazines.

If you love photography, you could volunteer to:

- Teach photography classes or workshops.
- Document events or projects in your community.
- Help set up photography exhibits or shows.
- Take photos for local nonprofits or organizations.
- Help run a community darkroom or photography lab.
- Take photos for a local charity's website or social media.

If sewing is what floats your boat, you could volunteer to:

- Teach sewing classes or workshops.

- Sew items for people in need, such as clothing, blankets or quilts.
- Mend or alter clothing for those who can't afford it.
- Make costumes or props for local theaters or schools.
- Sew items for a local animal shelter or wildlife rehabilitation center.
- Make simple toys or other items for children in need.
- Create craft kits or materials for senior centers or nursing homes.
- Make aprons or other protective gear for food pantries or soup kitchens.
- Make hats for those who have lost their hair to cancer.
- Make quilts or blankets for a hospital, maternity ward or homeless shelter.

If you love driving, perhaps you could:

- Drive people to and from medical appointments, treatment centers or food banks.
- Be a driver for Meals on Wheels or other food delivery programs.
- Drive for a ride-share service that provides rides to those in need.
- Drive people to the polls on election day.

- Transport animals for a local animal shelter or humane society.

If you love history, you could volunteer:

- At a historical society or museum.
- As a tour guide at a historical site or landmark.
- To transcribe historical documents or records.
- To help with an oral history project.
- To research and write about local history
- To help with a historical reenactment or living history event.

If you love writing, you could volunteer to:

- Write grant proposals for nonprofits or charities.
- Write newsletters or other materials for nonprofits or charities.
- Write articles for a local newspaper or online publication.
- Write or edit content for a website or blog.
- Help students with their writing skills.
- Write letters for a letter-writing campaign.

Do you love design? You could volunteer to:

- Help with website or app design.
- Design posters, fliers or other branding and marketing materials for local nonprofits or charities.
- Create social media graphics or other content for nonprofits or charities.
- Help with interior design for community spaces.
- Create t-shirt designs for a fundraising campaign.
- Help with the design of a new logo or branding for a local organization.

If organizing is in your blood, whether it's events or spaces, you could volunteer in:

- Straightening up a storage room, filing cabinet or closet for a nonprofit or charity.
- Organizing a donation drop-off site or area for a local nonprofit thrift shop.
- Helping out at your local library, returning the books to their proper places.
- Organizing an office space or filing system.
- Organizing the storage area for a local food bank.
- Helping with a non-profit or charity's administrative tasks or event planning.

- Organizing a fundraising drive or campaign.
- Helping a nonprofit or charity with database management.
- Organizing the storage and distribution of donations, such as clothing or food.
- Helping with the setup or break-down of a community event.
- The planning and execution of a community cleanup project.

If you are a person who is great at handling social media, you could volunteer to do the following kinds of things for a local non-profit, charity or school:

- Manage their social media accounts.
- Create content, such as photos, videos, or articles.
- Engage with followers, answer questions and respond to comments as a volunteer admin.
- Run social media campaigns or contests.
- Analyze and report on social media metrics.

If you love teaching, you could volunteer to:

- Help immigrant adults or children who are learning English as a second language.

- Teach various classes or workshops at a community center.
- Teach basic computer or internet skills to older adults.
- Teach cooking classes or nutrition education.
- Tutor students in an after-school program.
- Teach art or music classes to children or adults.

Do you just love to decorate? You could help decorate:

- A community space, like a library or food bank.
- A hospital or nursing home.
- A school or community center for a holiday or special event.
- For a wedding or other celebration for a low-income couple or family.
- For a local theater or production.
- Sets, props or costumes for a play or musical.
- Displays for a local art gallery or museum.
- For local seasonal festivals.

If you have a deep love of cars, trains, or boats, you could:

- Help restore classic cars, trains or boats for a museum or collection.
- Volunteer as a tour guide at a car, train or boat museum.

- Help organize or participate in a classic car, train or boat event.
- Participate in the restoration or maintenance of a historic car, train or boat.
- Work with a youth organization to teach kids about cars, trains or boats.
- Volunteer to help restore an old railroad station or depot, or car or boat museum.
- Help with ticket sales, operations or other aspects of running a local historical train.

If you have a knack for public speaking, you could:

- Deliver speeches or presentations for a charity or nonprofit.
- Host or emcee an event or fundraiser.
- Work as an advocate or spokesperson for a cause or organization.
- Work with a youth organization to teach kids about public speaking.
- Help organize or participate in a debate or speech contest, or volunteer to help out a local High School debate team when they are traveling to another city.

Do you love science? You could:

- Volunteer at a science museum or other educational facility.
- Assist with research or fieldwork for a scientific organization or institution.
- Work with a science communication organization, such as a science journalism group or science podcast.
- Volunteer with a citizen science project, such as those found on Zooniverse.
- Mentor or tutor students in science-related subjects.
- Help with science education programs in your community.
- Step up to be a volunteer docent at a history, science or aviation museum.

As you can see, there are endless opportunities for becoming a community volunteer as you're getting your sea legs in your new life of sobriety. One other area where you might help, when you feel ready and comfortable with the idea, is to share your recovery story with others. There are various ways you could choose to do this:

- Facilitating or hosting SMART Recovery meetings, which are based on a 4-point program and use evidence-based tools to help people overcome addictive behaviors.

- Joining the American Society of Addiction Medicine (ASAM), which is a professional organization that offers various volunteer opportunities for members and non-members to increase addiction prevention, treatment, remission and recovery.

If you are interested in volunteering in addiction recovery, you can start by exploring the websites of the organizations mentioned above or searching for other local or online options that suit your interests and availability. Volunteering can be a rewarding and meaningful way to support your own or someone else's recovery journey.

Last but certainly not least, helping someone else by sharing your own story in a recovery meeting, no matter what point you're at, can be a small way to help someone who has just started taking the first steps into their own new life!

CHAPTER 10 RESOURCES

- ***VolunteerMatch.org* website**: Matches inspired people with inspiring causes. It's how volunteers and nonprofits connect to achieve remarkable outcomes.
- ***Idealist.org* website**: "Explore our volunteer, event, and action listings to discover ways to make an impact in your community."
- ***PointsOfLight.org* website**: "There are hundreds of thousands of volunteer opportunities throughout the world waiting for the right volunteer to step up. Search our database for volunteer opportunities that meet critical needs. The world is waiting for you to shine your light."
- ***Volunteer.gov* website**: "Discover volunteer opportunities and learn how you can make an impact in causes you care about. Submit your volunteer application to thousands of sites across the country, all located at federal agencies that need your time and talent to meet their mission."
- ***Learn.GivePulse.com* website**: "Our mission is to enable everyone in the world to participate and become engaged in lifting their community to new

heights. We bring individuals and organizations together to drive social impact through a comprehensive giving platform. Find and register for causes and activities in your area. Track your volunteer hours, donations or impacts and verify your engagement."

- ***Zooniverse.org* website:** For those who love Science: "The Zooniverse is the world's largest and most popular platform for people-powered research. This research is made possible by volunteers - more than a million people around the world who come together to assist professional researchers."
- ***BeMyEyes.com* website:** Their mission is to make the world more accessible for 285 million people who are blind or have low vision.
- ***7Cups.com* website:** "7 Cups provides free, 24/7 emotional support to millions via online chat. We want to make sure nobody has to face their problems alone. Having someone like you to listen can be all it takes to make a real difference."

CHAPTER 11
Get An Education

You may not have ever thought about it this way, but education is not really about determining answers. It's about learning how to ask the right questions while giving you the focus, motivation, stability and sense of purpose you need to maintain your sobriety and live the fulfilling life you deserve.

As you pursue your education, you'll find yourself gaining more self-confidence and self-esteem, which in turn will help you stay motivated and committed to your recovery. You'll discover new social networks and support systems and increase job prospects and earning potential, which will provide additional stability and security.

JENNA'S TAKE

"It's never too late to pursue dreams or plans you may have lost along the way. I learned so much on my journey. And my mind, becoming clearer and more focused, consumed all the knowledge that was thrown at me. Most of it was very applicable to all aspects of my life, not just my sobriety.

So now what? My brain is still clean and focused. And with this newly found awakening I realize it's <u>never</u> too late to pursue those dreams and plans I had lost along the way. I have hopes to take a pottery workshop again, and I'm thinking of getting back into sign language. All things I did when I was younger. I think they will be enriching and fill my life with positivity. You only live once, learn to fly an airplane!!! Become an electrician!! Theater! And another positive result is, you'll make so many new friends along the way."

You might even learn new coping skills and stress management techniques (which can be especially helpful for people in early sobriety who may be dealing with a lot of stress and emotions). Education can help you to learn new ways of thinking and communicating, and improve your relationships and your everyday life. Then again, education can simply be enjoyable and fulfilling in and of itself, providing a sense of accomplishment and pride.

Education as a foundation for sobriety

At its core, education is about discovering new ideas and expanding your horizons. In sobriety, this can provide a great foundation for growth and change.

As you explore new concepts, you'll see the world in a new light, and that can help you stay committed to your sobriety. Education can give you the motivation and inspiration to continue on your journey of recovery, and can give you hope for a better future.

GOING BACK TO SCHOOL

For many people in early sobriety, going back to school can be a life-changing decision. It can provide a sense of purpose and direction, as well as a chance to learn new skills and develop new interests. It can also be a powerful source of structure and accountability, which can help keep you on track in your recovery.

We can imagine that many people in early sobriety may have mixed feelings about the idea of going back to school. But please understand: Education gives you the power to become your Best Self. It helps you build confidence, which in turn will help you stay committed to your sobriety and face any challenges that come your way. Education can be a source of light and hope in your life, and can lay the groundwork for growth and change.

GETTING YOUR GED

If getting your GED (or high school equivalency) needs to be the first step to getting an education, then go for it! Getting a GED can be accomplished in as little as 6 months to a year, and there are many different options, from online courses to in-person classes. So, choose one that fits your learning style and schedule.

Steps to getting your GED

- What is it? GED stands for 'General Education Development,' and it consists of four tests: Writing, Reading, Math and Science.
- Where is it? GED's are not offered through High Schools. They are offered through adult education centers, community colleges and correctional institutions. However, the local high school will know who to contact about getting your GED.
- Qualifying: The GED office will determine if you are eligible to register for getting your GED. Some common eligibility requirements are:

  - Residency: Most states require that you live in the state for a certain minimum length of time until you've attained "residency" and you're allowed to register to take the tests.
  - Minimum Age: Most states require that you be at least 16 to take the GED tests.
  - Waiting Period: Some states require a waiting period after dropping out of high school before you can register to take the tests.
- Registering is the next step to getting your GED. Here are the steps to get registered:
  - Find the GED website for your state.
  - Create an account (during this process you'll provide some basic personal information, such as your name, address and date of birth).
  - Pay the registration fee.

IMPORTANT NOTE

All states allow students to change the date of their GED tests. However, the specific policies and procedures for changing text dates vary from state to state.

- Schedule your tests. Most people schedule this about 6 months out. The website will probably have a list of available dates to choose from.

Here are some examples of how states handle test date changes (as of the date of this printing):

- **California:** Students can change their test date up to 14 days before the scheduled date. There is a $25 fee for changing the test date.
- **Florida:** Students can change their test date up to 24 hours before the scheduled date. There is no fee for changing the test date.
- **Texas:** Students can change their test date up to 30 days before the scheduled date. There is a $10 fee for changing the test date.

If you are unsure about the policies for changing test dates in your state, contact your local GED testing center.

Here are some tips for changing your GED test date:

- **Do it early:** The earlier you change your test date, the more likely you are to get a spot on the next available test date.
- **Be prepared to pay a fee:** Some states charge a fee for changing the test date.

- **Follow the instructions carefully:** Each state has its own procedures for changing the test date. Make sure you follow the instructions carefully to avoid any problems.

Changing your GED test date can be a hassle, but it is usually possible. By following the tips above, you can make the process as smooth as possible.

Preparing for the tests:

Here are some tips for preparing for the GED test

Create a study plan: Create a study plan that outlines what you need to learn and how much time you need to study.

Find a study buddy: Find a friend or family member who is also studying for the GED tests and study together.

Take practice tests: Take practice tests to get a feel for the types of questions you will be asked and to identify areas where you need to improve. You can find GED practice tests at GED.com.

Get help from a tutor: If you are struggling to learn the material, consider getting help from a tutor.

Here are some additional resources that can help you study for the GED tests:

- ***GED Ready:*** GED Ready is a free online practice test that can help you assess your readiness for the GED tests.
- ***GED Study Guide:*** The GED Study Guide is a free online study guide that can help you prepare for the GED tests.
- ***GED Course:*** There are many GED courses available online and in person that can help you prepare for the GED tests.

Here are some tips for taking the GED test:

- ***Arrive early:*** Arrive at the testing center at least 30 minutes before your scheduled test time.
- ***Bring the required materials:*** Bring your photo ID, admission ticket, and pencils or pens.
- ***Listen carefully to the instructions*** given by the test proctor and follow them carefully.
- ***Take your time:*** There is no need to rush through the test. Take your time and answer the questions carefully.

- ***Review your answers:*** After you have finished answering all of the questions, review your answers to make sure that you have answered them correctly.
- ***Don't give up:*** If you find the test to be difficult, don't give up. Keep working hard, and you will eventually pass the test.

Passing the GED test is a major accomplishment! It can open up many new opportunities for you, like getting a better job or going to college. With hard work and dedication, you'll achieve your goal of earning your high school equivalency diploma.

AFTER HIGH SCHOOL OR GED

If you have your high school or GED diploma, then you can go on to college if you wish to do so. College is a great way to further your education and prepare for a career. There are many different types of colleges, universities and technical schools; find one that fits your needs and interests.

Community College, University or Technical School?

First, think about your career goal and what type of education or training is required for that career. Do you want to be an electrician, plumber or carpenter? Technical school. A pharmacy tech, automotive specialist or web designer?

Certification through a community college. Biologist, anthropologist or engineer? 4-year university degree. To become a doctor or lawyer, you'll need additional schooling after university by going to medical school or law school.

Next, think about your budget and what you can afford. Community colleges and technical schools tend to be less expensive than universities. The schools can give you information about how to apply for grants and scholarships.

Finally, consider your own learning style and needs. Community colleges and technical schools often have smaller class sizes and more hands-on learning opportunities, while universities may have more opportunities for research and advanced study.

Characteristics of:

Universities – These are larger schools that offer a more traditional environment, more resources, more extracurricular activities and more degree options than community colleges or technical schools. Their focus is on critical thinking, problem-solving, research and advanced study. The class sizes are usually much larger, and the school can be more expensive, with less flexible scheduling options.

Community (or Junior) Colleges – Smaller class sizes, lower cost, often more focused on career or vocational training, more flexible schedule options and may offer online courses. In addition, some community colleges have what's called an "articulation agreement" with a university, which allows students to complete their general education requirements (first 2 years) at the community college, then transfer those credits to a university to complete a bachelor's degree. This can be a cost-effective way to earn a 4-year degree.

Technical or Trade Schools – These focus on specific job skills and offer more hands-on learning and a more structured and intensive environment than community college. They may also have shorter programs (6-12 months). There are many different types of technical and vocational schools. Some examples include trade schools, beauty schools, culinary schools, and medical schools.

- *Trade schools* offer training in specific fields like welding, plumbing, carpentry, and electrician work.
- *Beauty schools* teach students how to become hairdressers, nail technicians, makeup artists, and more.

- *Culinary schools* teach students how to become chefs, pastry chefs, and restaurant managers.
- *Medical schools* train students to become nurses, dental hygienists, massage therapists, and more.

There are many other opportunities, too, if you are not interested in committing a large amount of time and money to your education. Some of these alternative opportunities are:

- ***Online courses*** – Websites such as Udemy, Coursera, edX, Khan Academy, Brilliant, Alison, Skillshare and Codecademy each offer a wide range of courses on various topics.
    - Udemy is especially popular for courses in areas like business, design, marketing, and web development.
    - Coursera and edX offer courses from many well-known universities.
    - Brilliant focuses on teaching STEM (science, technology, engineering, and math) topics, with a focus on making these topics accessible and fun. The courses are self-paced, and they feature interactive elements and visual explanations.

    - Khan Academy, Alison, Skillshare and Codecademy are all focused on teaching specific skills, such as coding, web design, photography and IT.

- ***Auditing classes*** – When you audit a class, it means that you are attending the class and participating in the coursework but are not receiving a grade or credit for the course. You're essentially a guest in the class, and you don't have to worry about tests or assignments. This can be a good option if you are interested in the material but don't need credit, or if you want to try out a class before deciding whether to take it for credit.

  Universities and community colleges are more likely than private schools to offer auditing to their students. Check with the school you're interested in to see if this is something they offer.

- ***Local classes*** – Depending on the community you live in, there might be opportunities to take an array of different classes. In our community, there have been times when different individuals offered glassblowing, knitting/crocheting, guitar or piano lessons, among many others. Keep your eye on local publications to find these kinds of classes.

- ***Parks & Recreation classes*** – City Parks & Rec departments in many communities put out a seasonal catalog of classes, some even free.

- ***Attending lectures or seminars*** – It is common for universities and colleges to have Guest Lecturers or Seminars that are open to the public, sometimes for little or no fee. If you live in a college town, look up the events calendar on the school's website to track these down.

- ***Learning a new language*** – There are many great language-learning apps available. Some popular ones include Duolingo, Babbel, Memrise and Rosetta Stone. Each app has its own unique features and approach to language learning. For example, Duolingo uses a gamified approach with points, levels, and leaderboards, while Rosetta Stone focuses on immersion and uses no translation. Memrise is known for its spaced repetition system, and Babbel focuses on real-life conversation.

- ***YouTube*** – YT can be a great place not only to learn new stuff but to help you figure out what you'd like to do as a career before you commit to a community college, tech school or university.

- ***First Aid and CPR classes*** – Organizations like the American Red Cross, the American Heart Association, and the National Safety Council sometimes offer these classes for free or low-cost. Check out their websites to find local or online classes.

- ***MOOC's*** – This stands for "massive open online course." These are online courses that are offered for free to anyone who wants to take them. They are typically taught by professors from top universities and are available to anyone with an internet connection.

  Many different platforms offer MOOC's, such as edX, Coursera and FutureLearn. These courses cover a wide range of topics, from humanities to business to computer science.

Education is an amazing way to expand your horizons. It can be a form of self-care, a source of fulfillment and a path to personal growth.

Getting an education can also be a powerful tool for sobriety and recovery. It can provide a sense of purpose and structure, teach valuable skills, and connect you with new people and opportunities.

It's not always an easy journey, but the rewards can really be well worth it. Education can be a way to turn a new page in your life and start on a path to a happier, healthier future!

CHAPTER 11 RESOURCES

Getting Your GED

- ***GED.com*** – This website offers a variety of resources, including practice tests, tutorials and study guides. There are also tools to help you find a testing center and schedule your exam.
- ***GED Ready*** - "GED Ready" is a practice test available on GED.com. It's designed to help you prepare for the actual GED exam by providing a simulated experience and a score report. The score report shows how you performed in each of the four subject areas, and it provides recommendations for areas you might need to focus on in your studying.
- ***NOTE:*** GED Ready is not a requirement for taking the GED exam, but it can be a useful tool for identifying your strengths and weaknesses.
- ***GED Study Guide*** – You can find a GED study guide on the official GED website, as well as on other websites and online resources. For example, Khan Academy offers free study guides for the GED exam. You can also find study guides in bookstores or online retailers.

Choosing a School

- *CollegeBoard.org* – Types of Colleges (The Basics)
- *Indeed.com* – Community College vs. University: 11 Key Differences
- *CollegeVine.com* – Trade School vs. Community College: Which is Right for You?
- *Shane Hummus video* – College vs. Trade School
- *Shane Hummus video* – Trades Career Tier List (Trade Jobs Ranked)
- *Universal Technical Institute video* – College vs. Trade School vs. Community College: What's the Difference?

Other Online Venues

- *Udemy* – Udemy courses typically range in price from $10 to $200* The cost depends on the topic, the length of the course, and the instructor. However, Udemy often offers discounts and sales, so it's possible to find courses at a lower cost. They also offer a subscription option that allows you to access unlimited courses for a monthly or yearly fee*

- ***Coursera*** – Start, switch, or advance your career with more than 5,800 courses* professional certificates, and degrees from world-class universities and companies. The cost of Coursera courses varies depending on the topic and the length of the course. Some courses are available for free, while others have a fee ranging from $50 to $500* Like edX, Coursera offers both a free and paid track for each course, with the paid track offering additional features and the ability to earn a certificate of completion.*
- ***EdX*** – EdX courses typically range in price from $50 to $200* However, many of the courses are available for free if you opt for the audit track, which means you can view the course materials, but you won't earn a certificate of completion* The paid track allows you to earn a certificate of completion and may also offer additional features, such as graded assignments and access to a discussion forum.
- ***Khan Academy*** – All KA courses are offered for free* This is one of the key benefits of Khan Academy – it provides quality educational resources without a cost barrier. This makes it a great option

for those who want to learn something new but don't have the budget for a paid course. They offer courses in a wide range of topics, from math and science to history and economics.

- ***Brilliant*** – Fun, challenging problems on everything from logical reasoning to artificial neural networks. Brilliant's basic subscription costs $24.99 per month; the premium subscription costs $44.99 per month* These give you access to all the courses on the platform, of which there are approximately 70, mostly math, science and computer science. There's also a free 7-day trial available* so you can try the platform out before committing to a subscription.
- ***Alison*** – Alison offers free* courses in a wide variety of subjects, including business, technology, and personal development. The courses are self-paced, and there are no time limits for completion. You can also earn certificates of completion for many of the courses, which can be used to enhance your resume or demonstrate your skills to potential employers.
- ***YouTube*** – Whenever you need to learn about something specific, say, how to DIY plumb in a

dishwasher or how to start silversmithing, YouTube is a great place to start!

- ***Skillshare*** – An online learning platform that offers courses in various subjects, including business, marketing, technology, design, and writing. The courses are delivered in a video format and include project files, transcripts, and quizzes. Skillshare offers a monthly subscription for $15 per month or an annual subscription for $99 per year*
- ***CodeAcademy*** – A popular online learning platform for coding and web development. It offers courses in a variety of coding languages, including HTML, CSS, JavaScript, and Python. The courses are delivered in a step-by-step format and include interactive exercises and quizzes.
- Codeacademy offers a free plan and a pro plan, which costs $19.99 per month or $199.99 per year* The pro plan gives you access to additional features, like real-world projects and portfolio-building opportunities.
- **How to Audit a Class**: When you audit a class, you are essentially attending the class without enrolling and without earning a grade or credit. Instead, you

participate in the learning experience only. For many classes, auditing is not an official option, so it's important to talk to the professor or instructor before simply attending the class. Auditing is a great option for anyone who wants to expand their knowledge without committing to a grade or credit.

- **MOOC's:** Massive Open Online Courses (MOOC's) are free online courses available for anyone to enroll. MOOC's provide an affordable and flexible way to learn new skills, advance your career and deliver quality educational experiences at scale.

*As of the time of this printing.

CHAPTER 12

Take Care of Future You, too!

So, you've made it through the "acute" phase of recovery – Congratulations!

This chapter will be a round-up of what you've learned from this book and a discussion about what comes next in your life. It will talk about how you can go beyond just getting things under control and actually *planning* for the future. You have SO much life ahead of you now!

You've read about twelve ways to begin taking care of yourself and improving your life. These strategies are not meant to be completed all at once, but rather approached as a process of continuous improvement. As you work on each area of your life, you will find yourself becoming more confident, more capable and more prepared to handle whatever comes your way. We encourage you to start with small steps and then continue to build on your momentum. The future is yours to create – so figure out what 'success' means to you and go out there and make it great!

CHAPTER ONE – Nurture Your Mental Well-Being

Continue to nurture your mental health by practicing self-care, engaging in activities that bring you joy, connecting with loved ones and finding meaning and purpose in your life. This is not a one-time effort, though – it's an ongoing practice of creating a life that is fulfilling and rewarding.

Future Goals: What can you do to foster good mental health on into your future? Continue to prioritize self-care – remember to "Take Care of YOU!" This might include activities like journaling, meditation, exercise and healthy eating.

It's also important to maintain strong relationships with loved ones and to seek support when you need it. You can find purpose and meaning in your life by engaging in activities that align with your values. And finally, be sure to stay positive and practice gratitude – there is always something to be grateful for!

CHAPTER TWO – Learn to Say "No"

Chapter Two focused on the power of saying "No" without feeling guilty. This is a simple yet often overlooked skill that can have a huge impact on your life. As you get used to saying "No," you'll find it's easier to set boundaries, prioritize your time and energy and focus on the things that are most important to you. It will also help you avoid burnout and stress. Remember, saying "No" is not about being selfish or rude – it's about taking care of yourself and protecting your boundaries.

So, keep practicing saying "No" in low-stakes circumstances, and then gradually move on to more difficult situations. Use positive language and "I" statements when saying "No," such as "I'm sorry, but I won't be able to do that right now" or "I appreciate the offer, but I don't think it's the right fit for me." It's also important to remember that you don't owe anyone an explanation. By saying "No" assertively and respectfully, you will be setting healthy boundaries and taking care of YOU!

Future Goals: Once you've practiced and mastered saying "No," you're bound to feel a sense of empowerment and freedom. You may find that you're less stressed, more able to focus on the things that matter most to you and have more time and energy for the things you enjoy. You may even find that you feel more fulfilled and happier overall. So, keep setting those boundaries and being assertive!

CHAPTER THREE – Whip That Paperwork into Shape!

In the third chapter, you learned the importance of getting your paperwork in order or, in other words, taking care of the administrative side of your life. Keep your important documents organized; the longer you do it, the more used to it you'll become until it's second nature. While these tasks may not be the most exciting, they are essential for protecting yourself and your loved ones.

Future Goals: It is important to keep your mail and bills in good order. But as you move forward, there are a few more pieces of paperwork you might want to consider. First, make sure you have an Advance Directive in place, which outlines your wishes for medical treatment if you are unable to communicate them yourself.

Additionally, you may want to create both a Living Will, which outlines your wishes for end-of-life care, and a Power of Attorney, which gives someone else the authority to make decisions on your behalf if you become incapacitated. You may also consider setting up a Trust, which can help protect your assets and provide for your loved ones after you're gone.

CHAPTER FOUR – Take Care of Your Finances

While money can't buy happiness, it is a necessary part of life. Learning to take care of your finances is essential for protecting yourself and achieving your goals. It's important to create a budget and save for emergencies. You can also protect your financial well-being by avoiding excessive debt.

Future Goals: What we didn't discuss in Chapter 4 was investing and planning for retirement. As you become more proficient at taking care of your money, give some thought to both of these areas. And think about what you want to achieve financially in the future. Do you want to buy a house, retire early, or save for your child's education? Once you know what you want, you can start to make a plan to achieve it. You might want to find a good financial planner to help you out.

CHAPTER FIVE – Take Care of Your Body

Your body is the vehicle that you use to experience life, so it's really important to take care of it. That means eating healthy food, getting enough sleep, exercising regularly and managing stress. Taking care of your physical health will improve your mental and emotional health as well. It will also increase your energy levels and help you feel more confident.

Future Goals: As much as is feasible, keep increasing the amount of exercise you get, and keep getting better as a cook! Take managing stress seriously so that your future self will be more relaxed and able to cope with whatever life throws at you.

As you age, there are also a few additional health-related things you may want to put in place. First, make sure you have an easily accessible complete medical history, including a list of medications you're taking and any allergies you have. It's also important to designate a healthcare proxy, or someone who can make medical decisions on your behalf if you're unable to do so yourself.

CHAPTER SIX – Get Your Creativity On!

Creativity and play are an essential part of life, but they're often neglected as we get older. Making time for fun and self-expression can have a huge impact on your well-being. It can reduce stress, increase happiness, improve your problem-solving skills and provide a respite from the daily grind. So go ahead and schedule some time for play – your body, mind, and soul will thank you for it!

Future Goals: Once you've picked a creative outlet, take it further! Try something unexpected, like Brenda did with the oil paints. At first, the little negative voice in her head kept saying, "Hey, you tried this twice before, and you hated it." But instead of talking herself out of it, this time, she just went for it and found out it was fun! She created some things that she actually liked! So, she stretched in another direction and tried watercolors – and that turned out surprisingly well, too. Then she remembered that what she'd always been drawn to was doing pen and ink drawings, ever since she was a child. So, whenever she gets together with her friends to do art now, she's sketching and doing pen and ink.

You can do that, too! Whatever creative outlet you choose after reading Chapter Six, try expanding into new directions. Photography? Instead of just creating photos, why not try making a photo book or calendar? Music? Whatever instrument you've picked up, try different genres or get really brave and join in a jam session! Use your hobby to grow in new directions.

CHAPTER SEVEN – Take Care of Your Social Life

Chapter Seven was all about connection and communication – reconnecting with family, friends and the world around you. We really are social creatures, and our health and happiness can depend on our relationships. So, as you mend broken relationships, make sure to spend time with loved ones and reach out to new people.

Future Goals: Reconnecting with family, friends and colleagues is, of course, an important part of recovery. One way to expand on this is to participate in activities together that are focused on fun and connection. Make time for a family game night, a hike with friends or a group cooking class. The important thing is to keep focusing on building shared experiences and creating memories.

As you continue to repair and maintain your relationships, it's important to be intentional about your efforts. Consider setting aside regular time for your loved ones or friends, making an effort to be present in the moment. With time and effort, you will create deep, lasting connections with the people who are important in your life.

And as you get back into the working world, build and nurture a professional network. Attend industry events, join relevant organizations or communities, and connect with professionals in your desired field. Networking can provide opportunities, mentorship and valuable insights.

CHAPTER EIGHT – It Feels Good to Look Good!

Dressing well is not just about how you look. It's also about how you feel. Wearing clothes that make you feel confident and comfortable can impact your mood or even your accomplishments. No matter where you're going – the farm, the office or on a date – there's always room for style. So go ahead and put on that favorite outfit, even if it's just for running errands. You deserve to feel good every day!

Future Goals: Dressing well will have a positive impact on your life, both now and in the future. It will boost your confidence and your self-esteem, leading to better opportunities and more fulfilling relationships. As you continue to build your sense of style, be sure to focus on finding clothes that make you feel good and reflect your personal taste. Over time, your style may evolve and change, but the key is to always stay true to yourself and what makes you happy.

CHAPTER NINE – Take Care of the Legal Stuff

Facing up to the legal consequences of your addiction is one of the most important steps in moving forward with your recovery. By taking responsibility for your actions, you'll start making amends and rebuilding trust. It's not always easy, but it's definitely worth the effort!

Future Goals: Try to think forward to the time when your legal stuff is far behind you. You took responsibility for your actions and faced the legal consequences. You may have felt scared or uncertain, but now you can see what an important step it was in moving forward. And even though it was difficult, you were not alone – some people helped and supported you all along the way. With their help, you got through that challenging time and moved on to a brighter future where your conscience is clean, and you rightly feel a confidence that you never had before!

CHAPTER TEN – Give Back to the World

When you're giving back to the world, you're not only helping others, you're also helping yourself! Volunteering in your community will reduce your stress, improve your mood, and even boost your physical health. It's also a great way to connect with others and feel a sense of belonging. Now that you've learned and experienced the benefits of volunteering, you understand that you can give back to the world in many different ways, from lending a helping hand to simply smiling at a stranger.

Future Goals: As you continue giving your time and energy to your chosen cause, you may find that your life is becoming more and more meaningful and fulfilling. Maybe you'll start feeling more connected to others and have a greater sense of purpose. As you experience the positive impact of your service, you may even find that you are inspired to do more and give back in new ways – perhaps even taking on a leadership role. Your journey of giving back can be a lifelong one, full of growth, learning, and even joy!

CHAPTER ELEVEN – Get an Education

Education is one of the most powerful tools you have for changing your life because it will open up new opportunities and help you grow in ways you've never imagined. Whether you choose to go to school, take an online course, or simply read a book, there are endless possibilities for educating yourself. And best of all, you don't have to limit yourself to traditional educational paths. You can learn about anything that interests you.

Future Goals: As you continue your educational journey, your life will expand in new and exciting ways. You'll gain new skills and knowledge and be able to apply them in your daily life. You may find that your relationships improve as you have more to talk about and share with others. You may even discover a new career path or passion that you never knew was possible!

So, embrace a lifelong learning mindset. Stay curious, seek knowledge, and develop new skills relevant to your interests and career aspirations. Take courses, attend workshops, read books, and explore online resources.

In addition to each of the above-suggested ways to keep on track in the future, don't forget you can also:

- ***Keep setting new goals***: Setting new goals, no matter how small, can help you maintain momentum and keep moving forward, so set new ones as you get through your current goals.
- ***Keep up with self-care:*** Self-care is not a luxury. It's a necessity – make it a regular part of your routine, and don't feel guilty about taking time for yourself.
- ***Keep growing as a person***: Growth is a lifelong process - make a commitment to continue learning and evolving as a person.
- ***Make a bucket list***: Creating a bucket list of all the things you want to do in your life will give you a sense of purpose and excitement.
- ***Explore new hobbies***: Trying out new hobbies is a great way to expand your horizons and discover new passions. Don't be afraid to experiment with different activities.
- ***Identify what success looks like*** to you rather than following someone else's idea of success.

- ***Stay connected to your support network***: Make an effort to stay connected with the people who support and encourage you, and don't be afraid to ask for help when you need it.
- ***Make a record of your successes and failures***: Journaling can be a powerful tool for self-reflection and self-discovery – it's a way to explore your thoughts and feelings in a safe and private space.
- ***Keep practicing the new skills you've learned***. Practice gratitude, continue your education, keep getting to know yourself better, and hone your boundary-setting skills.

As your journey continues, remember that recovery is a lifelong process. It's not always easy, but the effort is always worth it. By taking care of all aspects of yourself, you are laying the foundation for a happy, healthy life.

Plan and Reflect: Regularly review and adjust your plans as needed. Reflect on your progress, learn from failures, and celebrate achievements. Keep your goals in sight and make necessary modifications along the way.

With help and support from friends, family and professionals, you can overcome any challenges that come your way and create the life you've always wanted. Be kind to yourself, be open to new opportunities, and keep on learning. Most importantly, never give up! You are stronger than you think, and you are worthy of all the good things in life. Keep your eyes on the horizon and keep moving forward.

Your best days are yet to come!

HELPFUL RESOURCES

Nia.Nih.gov article "Getting Your Affairs in Order Checklist: Documents to Prepare for the Future"

MeetUp.com **website**: I repeat this link here because what an amazing way to meet new people and find fun sober activities!

BurningTree.com article: "Organization Skills for Sobriety and Well-being"

Coursera.org article: "What Are Leadership Skills, and Why Are They Important?

Insider Business video: "5 Easy Steps to Follow to Reach Your Financial Goals"

Printed in Great Britain
by Amazon